Learning Activities
from the
History of Mathematics

Frank J. Swetz

J. Weston Walch, Publisher
Portland, Maine

User's Guide
to
Walch Reproducible Books

As part of our general effort to provide educational materials which are as practical and economical as possible, we have designated this publication a "reproducible book." The designation means that purchase of the book includes purchase of the right to limited reproduction of all pages on which this symbol appears:

Here is the basic Walch policy: We grant to individual purchasers of this book the right to make sufficient copies of reproducible pages for use by all students of a single teacher. This permission is limited to a single teacher, and does not apply to entire schools or school systems, so institutions purchasing the book should pass the permission on to a single teacher. Copying of the book or its parts for resale is prohibited.

Any questions regarding this policy or requests to purchase further reproduction rights should be addressed to:

Permissions Editor
J. Weston Walch, Publisher
321 Valley Street • P. O. Box 658
Portland, Maine 04104-0658

—J. Weston Walch, Publisher

The Historical Sketch Report Form and sample on pages 80 and 81 appear courtesy of Art V. Johnson of Nashua Senior High School, Nashua, New Hampshire.

1   2   3   4   5   6   7   8   9   10
ISBN 0-8251-2264-3
Copyright © 1994
J. Weston Walch, Publisher
P. O. Box 658 • Portland, Maine 04104-0658
Printed in the United States of America

Contents

Introduction

In suggesting new mathematics curricula and instruction methodologies to accommodate America's transition from an industrial to an informational society, the National Council of Teachers of Mathematics (NCTM) emphasizes the importance of historical perspectives in mathematics teaching. Among the new goals for students listed in the Council's *Curriculum and Evaluation Standards for School Mathematics*, the very first goal, "Learning to Value Mathematics," specifies:

> *Students should have numerous and varied experiences related to the cultural, historical, and scientific evolution of mathematics so that they can appreciate the role of mathematics in the development of our contemporary society and explore relationships among mathematics and the disciplines it serves: the physical and life sciences, the social sciences, and the humanities....It is the intent of this goal—learning to value mathematics—to focus attention on the need for student awareness of the interaction between mathematics and the historical situations from which it has developed and the impact that interaction has on our culture and our lives.*

Quite simply these statements affirm the importance of associating the teaching of mathematics with its history.

This concept is not new; it has been around for a long time. A century ago (1890) in marking another societal transitional period—that of moving from an agricultural society to an industrial one, and the place of mathematics in that movement—J. W. L. Glaisher, president of the British Association for the Advancement of Science, noted that "no subject loses more than mathematics by any attempt to dissociate it from its history." Acknowledging this concept and putting it into action are two different things, however. While influential people and organizations can proclaim the importance of the history of mathematics, it remains for us as classroom teachers to implement this association. Many teachers have indeed taken up the task. The NCTM's first Yearbook, published in 1926, describes the efforts of an Ohio teacher who challenged her 7th- and 8th-grade students with such questions as "Who was Thales?" and "Where did the signs +, −, ×, ÷, and = come from?" Such questions would be equally challenging and interesting today. However, efforts to use a historical outlook are often isolated and the result of the creative outlook of individual teachers. Neither methods courses nor texts usually discuss the techniques or pedagogy of incorporating historical material with the teaching of mathematics.

For many years I have worked with teachers and students in trying to overcome this problem. Together we have learned some of the methods and strategies that successfully incorporate mathematics with its history—strategies and methods worth sharing. This manual is intended for the purposes of that sharing. It is a reference handbook with suggested activities and materials to use, problems, and bibliographies that should be of value to any mathematics teacher who wishes to enrich his or her teaching. As such, this book is not comprehensive but is rather intended to be a resource guide of ideas that you the teacher can use or modify depending on your particular needs. The contents discuss what has worked in many classrooms. We hope they will work in many more.

—Frank Swetz

CHAPTER 1

Teaching Strategies

The history of mathematics is exhilarating, because it unfolds before us the vision of an endless series of victories of the human mind....

—George Sarton, noted historian of science

"I know that the history of mathematics is important, but I just haven't got the time to teach another topic in my classes" is often the reply given by a teacher when asked about his or her use of the history of mathematics. What with oversized classes and a crowded curriculum, many teachers are already overburdened with work and reluctant to take on an "extra," like teaching about the history of mathematics. But the history of mathematics should not be seen as an "extra." It should be appreciated as a fundamental part of mathematics instruction, which can add to and enrich the overall study of the subject and contribute to a better understanding of mathematics and its concepts, development, and uses. Unfortunately, it is easy to get into a rut and teach mathematics as a collection of symbols and procedures designed to produce answers for a given set of problems without really teaching "about mathematics": where it comes from, how it was labored on, and how its theories were refined and developed—in brief, its social and human relevance. As a result of this practice, some students become overwhelmed by mathematics, which appears to them as an incomprehensible collection of rules and formulas. These students become alienated from the subject and acquire anxieties over using mathematics.

The history of mathematics supplies human roots to the subject. It associates mathematics with people and their needs. It humanizes the subject and, in doing so, removes some of its mystique. Mathematics isn't something magic and forbiddingly alien; rather, it's a body of knowledge developed by people over a 10,000-year period. These people, just like us and our students, made mistakes and were often puzzled, but they persisted and worked out solutions for their problems. Mathematics is and always was people-centered. Its teaching should recognize and build on this fact by incorporating the history of mathematics as a fundamental part of its learning.

It's best to include the history of mathematics naturally in lessons. Don't view it as something extra, but rather as a complement to mathematics learning, a background, a perspective that helps clarify the topic under discussion. Students must clearly see the connections between the mathematics they are studying and the relevant historical facts. How best to do this? Over the years various teachers have successfully used several strategies to incorporate the history of mathematics into its teaching. Of course, teaching and learning are very personal experiences, and what might work for one teacher or class will not necessarily work for others. Appropriate strategies are described and briefly discussed below. Following chapters enlarge upon each strategy and supply materials and resources to help carry out the particular strategy in question.

Historically based teaching strategies that have worked with varied student audiences include:

1. A consideration of the people of mathematics—the lives and work of selected mathematical personages.

2. Obtaining information about the origins and meanings of mathematical terms, symbols, and words.

3. Assigning classical or historical problems and noting their origins or significance.

4. Carrying out activities based on historical problems or discoveries.

5. Using historically based films or videotapes in classroom instruction.

Consideration of the lives and work of past (and present) mathematicians reaffirms the human face of mathematics, the fact that mathematics is developed by people—people who, in most respects are just like us. Often they failed in their attempts to solve a particular problem; perhaps they tried again or others took up the challenge and eventually found the required solution or even a solution for a problem not originally considered. In viewing the lives of famous mathematicians, we are struck by the fact that frequently it was not so much the individual's genius that resulted in accomplishments and discoveries, but rather that person's persistence. Students are encouraged and reassured by such information.

You can reveal the lives of famous mathematicians to students in many ways: for example, by using historical sketches, posters, and charts that refer to the lives and work of these mathematicians, and by assigning student readings and reports on the subject.

Mathematics has sometimes been described as a subject that has its own language. To some extent this is true; mathematics does have its own symbols and words, and part of the learning of mathematics involves using this vocabulary. Some texts list mathematics vocabulary in special sections intended for study. These words and symbols should not be viewed as stumbling blocks in the process of learning; rather, they should be signposts on the path to understanding the concepts or procedures under discussion. Each mathematical term and symbol has a history, a story behind it. I have found that students as well as teachers often enjoy knowing this history and appreciating how it relates to the mathematics they are doing. Just a simple teaching act, explaining the origin of a word, can have a profound learning impact for students.

We are always looking for good problems to strengthen and broaden our students' knowledge of mathematics as well as to refine concepts taught in the classroom. The history of mathematics supplies thousands of useful and interesting problems, problems that are mathematically and pedagogically sound and which, by their historical nature, possess an additional intellectual appeal for students. Instructional use of such problems is a very easy classroom innovation to institute.

Activities involving the duplication of historical experiences and events allow students to participate actively in making mathematical discoveries. Several activity situations that easily come to mind and that can be carried out at the secondary level are: obtaining a numerical estimation for π, using Eratosthenes' technique to determine the circumference of the earth, solving algebraic equations by using geometric techniques, and performing classical Greek ruler-and-compass constructions. Through such activities, students begin to understand the experimental nature of mathematical inquiry and also appreciate the mathematical creativity of our ancestors. You can use activities like this with a class to introduce a concept, to reinforce it, or to supply enrichment.

The history of mathematics is broad in scope and very rich in content. Even the most knowledgeable and dynamic of teachers may experience difficulties in adequately capturing the drama and color of a mathematical event or discovery. Visual aids can help overcome this problem and, within themselves, become a source of mathematics learning. Students can touch the history of mathematics by reading a page from a 15th-century arithmetic book or discussing the implications of a geometric illustration drawn perhaps hundreds of years ago. A picture of an Egyptian hieroglyphic inscription reveals that its writers were concerned with the properties of an isosceles triangle. To student viewers, this can become an enlightening statement of the universality of mathematical concepts over time and place. A good selection of commercial films and videotapes devoted to the history of mathematics exists for classroom use. This media is the end product of prolonged planning and careful utilization of available visual resources, such as artifacts and locations, and provides a convenient and efficient means of surveying happenings in the history of mathematics. Chapter 6 of this book, "One Picture Is Worth…," contains a selected listing of these films and videotapes.

For the most part, the strategies just reviewed are flexible and lend themselves to several modes of teaching, such as introducing a concept, reinforcing and strengthening the knowledge and understanding of a concept already learned, or providing an opportunity for enrichment and individual learning. You can incorporate these strategies into your classroom lesson or let them serve as a focus for extracurricular activities—for example, in the functioning of student mathematics clubs or as the basis for student projects and term reports.

If you are interested in using the history of mathematics as an instructional complement, you should experiment with different strategies and decide which are the best for your classes and expand and develop those strategies as required.

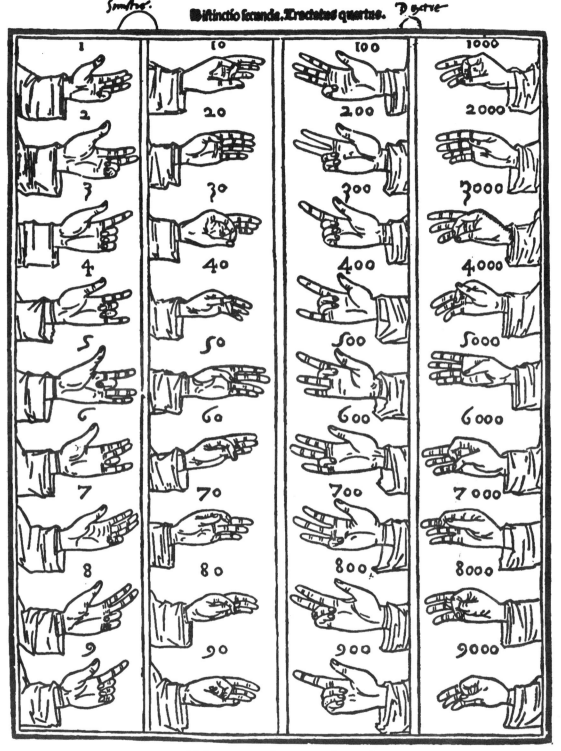

15th-century finger mathematics

CHAPTER 2

The People of Mathematics

While many terms have been applied to mathematics—an art, a science, the Queen of the Sciences, a game played with rules we do not fully understand—ultimately it is a human experience. Far too often the humanity of mathematics is forgotten in its classroom teaching. Students may learn some mathematical facts and some rules and procedures by which to apply them to a set of numbers or a geometrical figure, but frequently students are not quite sure just why and for what purpose these rules and procedures have been derived. This is where the history of mathematics can most effectively come into play: It can associate names, faces, and situations with particular concepts and procedures; it can identify the results learned in class as a human effort directed at solving a human need and associated with a particular person or group of people. Mathematics should not be anonymous. It should have an identity associated with people.

True, students may recognize some historical names such as Euclid, Pythagoras, or Descartes, but unfortunately, students' further understanding of the significance of these names is usually limited. To know that Euclid (ca. 300 B.C.) has something to do with geometry (no, he did not invent it) is reassuring, but how much more meaningful it would be if those students realized that Euclid's 13 books on *Elements* cover far more than geometry and represent the consolidation and systematization of 300 years of Greek mathematical experimentation and discovery. Aha! Mathematics occasionally needs to be consolidated and organized—a major realization. Associating Pythagoras with the right triangle is noteworthy, but better yet is the recognition of the Pythagoreans' concern with numerical harmony and their eventual confrontation with irrational numbers. René Descartes (1596–1650) may be credited with the popularization of the rectangular coordinate system, but how much more satisfying it would be to learn how he employed a concept of coordinates to bind geometry together with algebra and develop the discipline of analytic geometry. You can and should unfold these scenarios before your students.

The drama, suspense, and intrigue of mathematics—features that appeal to most audiences, including students—most often rest with the people of mathematics, the doers and movers in the history of mathematics. The Tartaglia–Cardano dispute demonstrates human foibles but also highlights the importance of algebraic computation in the 15th century. The failed attempts of Hippocrates of Chios (ca. 440 B.C.) to square the circle and solve a classical problem of Greek antiquity illustrate ingenuity and mathematical insights that were of value in themselves. Hippocrates' quest was carried on by other mathematical adventurers including Leonardo da Vinci (1452–1519). Was this problem ever solved? If not, why? Did François Viète's (1540–1603) concern with secret codes figure in his attempts to develop a symbolic language for algebra? Why were the letter-writing efforts of Marin Mersenne (1588–1648) a stimulus to mathematical advances in the 17th century? Who "invented" the calculus first, Isaac Newton (1642–1727) or Gottfried Wilhelm Leibniz (1646–1716), and why did this controversy split the European mathematical community? Who was the mysterious Monsieur Le Blanc, and what was his relationship to Carl Friedrich Gauss (1777–1855)? What is the Russell paradox, and who is the Gödel of Gödel's proof? In seeking answers to such questions, a student learns much about mathematics and develops a fuller appreciation of its significance. Techniques you can use with a class that will help to acquaint students with the people of mathematics include using anecdotes and brief historical sketches and assigning reports and research projects.

Using Anecdotes and Brief Historical Sketches

The injection of one or more brief historical anecdotes during a class discussion offers a change of pace from the usual teacher–student interaction. It can be amusing, informative, and thought-provoking and set the stage for further mathematical discussion and learning. As an example, consider the story involving the young Gauss, the so-called Prince of Mathematicians, who at age ten was given the task by a teacher of finding the sum for the natural numbers from 1 to 100. His teacher thought this problem would keep the class occupied for some time (busywork is not new) and was amazed when Gauss quickly made a mental calculation and supplied the correct answer, 5,050. The young boy had noted this pattern:

$$
\begin{array}{r}
1 + 2 + 3 + \ldots + 98 + 99 + 100 \\
+ (100 + 99 + 98 + \ldots + 3 + 2 + 1) \\
\hline
101 + 101 + 101 + \ldots + 101 + 101 + 101 = 100\,(101)
\end{array}
$$

Realizing he had obtained twice the required sum, Gauss modified his answer by dividing by 2:

$$
\frac{(100)\,(101)}{2} = 5{,}050
$$

This simple story emphasizes the importance of looking at mathematics: seeking patterns and, if possible, using those patterns to solve a problem. While a powerful lesson in problem-solving has been carried out, further considerations and questions easily evolve: "Does the technique work for any consecutive series of numbers?" "Would it work for a series of even numbers?" "Can the class generalize a formula to encompass the process?" and so on.

Numerous other anecdotes are available to reflect on varied aspects of mathematics. Consider the instance when Johannes Müller (1436–1476), an accomplished German mathematician sometimes known as Regiomontanus, was challenged to a contest by a draftsman who wished to test Müller's geometric ability. The contest was the ruler and compass construction of right triangles—the man who correctly constructed the most right triangles within a fixed period of time would be the winner. Müller easily won by initially constructing a semicircle and rapidly inscribing triangles in it using its diameter as a fixed side of the required triangles. He utilized the principle that all triangles inscribed in a semicircle are right triangles. While this story is not profound in itself, it reinforces and amplifies the right triangle/semicircle concept.

The importance of inquisitiveness combined with observation and mathematical experimentation can be conveyed by describing the 1581 experiences of Galileo Galilei (1564–1642) in observing a swinging altar lamp in the cathedral at Pisa. He timed the period for an arc of the lamp's swing by using his own heartbeats as a measure of time and discovered that the period of oscillation for a swinging body was independent of the arc length traveled. This principle became the basis for the development of the pendulum clock. Galileo employed such experimental practices throughout his scientific life. His dropping of two different-sized weights from the leaning tower of Pisa to resolve the law that the distance a body falls is proportional to the square of the time in flight, irrespective of the weight, has inspired several of my students to duplicate this experiment. (Much to their satisfaction and my relief, they affirmed Galileo's findings.)

Every teacher can easily accumulate a few favorite anecdotes relevant to his or her teaching situation, ones that pertain to the mathematics being taught and reveal the human side of mathematics while telling the listener something about mathematics itself.

Anecdotes are usually told orally, which demands a teacher's time and preparation. An easier method of bringing the people of mathematics to a class is through the use of brief historical sketches. The historical sketch is a printed presentation that identifies a mathematician or a mathematical accomplishment and then goes on to tell the reader some facts about the subject. Such sketches, when dealing with people, are often accompanied by a picture of the particular person in question. A sketch must be brief (one printed page), concise, easy to read, and appealing in some manner. Cartoons are frequently incorporated. Sketches like these lend themselves to use as classroom posters. Sets of sketches can be commercially purchased or constructed by teachers and students. In fact, a worthwhile learning project is to have students construct a set of historical posters that will eventually be displayed for viewing.

A sample set of historical poster sketches are included in the following pages. They are intended for possible classroom use. This set was devised and written with several learning factors in mind:

1. Each person depicted and discussed made an important contribution to the development of mathematics.

2. The contributions described span the various branches of mathematics and are chronologically distributed over the history of mathematics.

3. The selection of personages is representative of the diverse, multicultural nature of mathematical contributions.

The posters can be a source of either passive learning (students can read them individually as they wish) or active learning (direct questions can be asked and activities focused around a poster's subject). For illustrative purposes and possible use, a brief set of sample questions is included for each poster.

Thales (ca. 640–546 B.C.)

The First Mathematician

About 640–546 B.C.

Photo courtesy of the New York Public Library

Of course it is impossible really to name the *first* mathematician, that is, the very first person who used mathematics extensively in daily life. Perhaps this person was a tribal leader who kept a careful count of the wild game his or her hunting band had bagged or a shaman who carefully noted the positions of the moon as an indicator for the people to migrate to better pasturelands. Whoever this person was, he or she remains unknown. Written history does, however, recognize a single individual as the first mathematician. He is the Greek named Thales of Miletus who lived around 600 B.C. At that time, Miletus was a flourishing Greek colony on the coast of Asia Minor and a thriving trading center. Perhaps Thales' family were merchants, but he himself appears to have been a self-made man who used his talents to great advantage in the worlds of both commerce and science and mathematics.

Many stories are told about Thales. One story reveals that as a young man Thales was very poor and a friend, sharing his poverty, lamented on their status by remarking, "If one is born poor, then one will remain poor for the rest of his life." Thales disagreed strongly, saying that if he set his mind to the task, he could become rich. He challenged his friend to give him six months to accomplish this feat. Six months later, the friend returned to find Thales a wealthy man. He had foreseen a good olive harvest and went about the region leasing all available olive presses, the devices needed to make olive oil, an important food in the Greek diet. When the

Learning Activities from the History of Mathematics

good crop came in, Thales controlled all the olive presses and in turn the production of olive oil. The fees he charged for rendering the olives into oil with his presses made him a wealthy man and established him as both an entrepreneur and a merchant.

As a merchant, Thales traveled widely and became a keen observer of the customs and knowledge of neighboring peoples. In Babylonia he learned the techniques of astronomy, and in Egypt he was impressed by the geometric skills of the priest-surveyors who reestablished land boundaries after each annual flooding of the Nile River. While in Egypt, Thales demonstrated his own geometric skills by determining the height of the Great Pyramid of Giza by methods of indirect measurement. By comparing the pyramid's shadow with that of an object of known height and utilizing the property of similar triangles that corresponding sides are in proportion, Thales was able to find the unknown height.

Eventually, he returned to Miletus, retired from the commercial world, and devoted himself to studying and teaching philosophy, mathematics, and science. He brought together all the information he had learned about foreign mathematics and developed it into a systematic body of knowledge.

In particular, history credits Thales with providing proofs for several basic geometric propositions:

1. A circle is bisected by its diameter.

2. Every angle inscribed in a semicircle is a right angle.

3. If two straight lines intersect, the opposite angles formed are congruent.

4. The base angles of an isosceles triangle are equal.

5. The sides of similar triangles are proportional.

6. Two triangles are congruent if they have two angles and a side respectively congruent.

It was through such efforts that Thales became known as the first mathematician. Further, Thales was greatly admired for his wisdom and is supposed to have originated the saying that in seeking wisdom one must first "know thyself." Once when asked what was the strangest thing he had seen in all his travels, he replied, "An aged tyrant." Thales never married. He was further honored by later Greek generations by being chosen as the first of the Seven Wise Men of Antiquity, the only mathematician in this famous company.

Name _____ Date _____

Thales of Miletus

The following questions and investigations are intended to broaden a historical under-standing of the persons and issues examined. They should provoke thinking and guide further research on the subjects under discussion. In several instances, library resources may have to be consulted.

1. Thales was born in Miletus in Asia Minor. Today, in what country would we find the birthplace of Thales?

   _____

   _____

   _____

2. In Egypt, Thales observed priest-surveyors at work. Why would priests be doing surveying?

   _____

   _____

   _____

3. How do you think Thales used geometric knowledge to determine the height of the Great Pyramid? Remember, he could not climb to the top of the pyramid.

   _____

   _____

   _____

4. Thales said that in seeking wisdom you must first "know thyself." What did he mean?

   _____

   _____

   _____

5. Thales was one of the Seven Wise Men of Antiquity. Name three other men in this group.

   _____

   _____

   _____

Pythagoras (ca. 580–500 B.C.) and the Pythagoreans

Mathematics and Mysticism

About 580–500 B.C.

Pythagoras was born about 580 B.C. on the island of Samos in the Aegean Sea. He left home at an early age and wandered for many years throughout the countries of the East, perhaps traveling as far as India. When he was approximately 50 years old, he returned home, settled in Crotona, a Greek colony in southern Italy, and founded a school devoted to the study of a mystical philosophy based on the concept that everything is controlled by numbers— whole numbers.

Pythagoras' teachings attracted student disciples who formed into a brotherhood or fraternity. The brotherhood had a strict set of rules and rituals. Pythagoreans, as they were called, could not eat meat or beans, drink wine, wear wool, or touch a white rooster. They believed in the transmigration of souls, thus the rules against eating meat and wearing wool—the animals these products came from may have been former friends. One story relates how Pythagoras came upon a man beating his dog and urged him to stop, saying, "In this dog lives the soul of my friend; I recognize him by his voice." The man stopped beating his dog.

In seeking mathematical harmony with the universe, the Pythagoreans studied *arithmetica*, the properties of numbers (number theory), music, astronomy, and geometry. Each of these subjects depended on the use of numbers. For example, Pythagoras taught that all matter was composed of four elements: fire, represented by the number 1; water, 2; air, 3; and earth, 4. These were the *holy tetracyts*

whose sum $(1 + 2 + 3 + 4 = 10)$ was the number of the universe. Numbers could have many meanings, which in turn were used to form relationships. For example, 2 was the female number; joining it with 3, the male number, resulted in 5, the number for marriage; 6 was the number for creation (the universe was created in six days); 4 represented justice (a square deal). Also, 6 was a perfect number, being the sum of its proper factors $(1 + 2 + 3 = 6)$; numbers smaller than the sum of their proper factors were called deficient numbers, and those larger were called abundant numbers. Pairs of numbers for which each is the sum of the proper factors of the other number were called amicable numbers. For example, 220 and 284 are amicable numbers. The Pythagoreans were also involved with figurative numbers, that is, numbers formed by a geometric arrangement of dots. The geometric arrangement lent itself to devising names for the numbers. Thus, there were triangular numbers $(1, 3, 6, \ldots)$, square numbers $(1, 4, 9, \ldots)$, pentagonal numbers $(1, 5, 12, \ldots)$, and so on. The sign for the society of Pythagoreans was the five-pointed star, or pentagram. This geometrical figure had mystical properties: A series of smaller pentagrams could be constructed inside a given pentagram, and the legs of a pentagram are divided numerically according to the golden ratio.

In the history of mathematics, the Pythagoreans are noted for two major discoveries: the existence of irrational numbers, that is, numbers whose magnitude could not be expressed as a ratio of two whole numbers, and the numerical relationship for the sides of a right triangle. This latter accomplishment is usually called the Pythagorean theorem, but it is now known that Pythagoras and the Pythagoreans were not the first to discover this geometric theorem.

Legend relates how Pythagoras was killed by a mob when he was about 80 years old—he could have escaped, but refused to tread on a sacred bean field. The school he founded and the Pythagorean brotherhood continued for several centuries after the master's death.

Name _____ Date _____

Questions and Investigations

Pythagoras and the Pythagoreans

      The following questions and investigations are intended to broaden a historical understanding of the persons and issues examined. They should provoke thinking and guide further research on the subjects under discussion. In several instances, library resources may have to be consulted.

1. The Pythagoreans believed in the transmigration of the soul. What does this mean? Do any people today also believe in this principle?

    _____

    _____

    _____

2. Pythagoras thought that music was ruled by numbers. Do you agree with him? Explain your answer.

    _____

    _____

    _____

3. Find two perfect numbers other than 6. List three deficient and three abundant numbers.

    _____

    _____

    _____

4. If the Pythagoreans were really not the first people to know that the sum of the squares of the sides of a right triangle equal the square of the hypotenuse, who probably were the first people to know this important mathematical fact?

    _____

    _____

    _____

5. The discovery of irrational numbers by the Pythagoreans caused them great concern. Why should this fact have troubled them?

    _____

    _____

    _____

© 1994 J. Weston Walch, Publisher   *16*   *Learning Activities from the History of Mathematics*

Euclid (ca. 300 B.C.)

The Geometer and His Elements

About 300 B.C.

The greatest mathematical textbook of all time is the *Elements*, written by Euclid of Alexandria in the period 320–260 B.C. In the Western world, this book's popularity is exceeded only by the Bible. For over 2,000 years, its contents have dictated the study of geometry. It is strange that for so famous a book, little is actually known about its author. Euclid was a mathematician at the Museum in Alexandria. From the 4th century B.C. to about the 3rd century A.D., Alexandria and its museum (more like a university by modern standards) were the center of Greek learning. Euclid researched, taught, and wrote about mathematics. Eventually, he published ten books, of which the *Elements* is most renowned.

Several stories tell about Euclid's regard for geometry and its learning. One story notes how Soter, the first king of Egypt and founder of the museum, while studying geometry under Euclid found it difficult and asked for an easier way to learn the subject. Euclid replied, "Oh, King, in the real world there are two kinds of roads: roads for the common people to travel upon and roads reserved for the king to travel upon. In geometry there is no royal road." Another time, Euclid was asked by a student, "What is the value of learning geometry?" In response, Euclid requested a slave to give the student a coin so that he could "make gain from what he learns."

The word *elements* for the Greeks meant "basics" or "foundations." Thus, the *Elements* is a survey of the basic mathematics known in Euclid's time. What has made the *Elements* so popular is its logical organization. Beginning with 23 definitions, 5 axioms, and 5 postulates, Euclid systematically built up the mathematics he discussed, producing 465 propositions or theorems with their proofs. Actually, in its original form the *Elements* consisted of 13 books, each with its own emphasis, and covered not only topics in geometry but also topics in algebra and number theory. The geometry taught in high schools today usually includes the material contained in Books I, III, IV, VI, XI, and XII of the *Elements*.

Over 1,000 editions of the *Elements* have been published. No original copy exists, and for many years the oldest known copy—from which other copies were produced—was written by Theon of Alexandria in A.D. 365 Theon's Greek edition was translated into Arabic and later during the Middle Ages was reintroduced into Europe in Latin. Thus, for a long time Theon's edition was the sole source

of knowledge of Euclid's *Elements*. In 1808 the French scholar François Peyrard discovered an older copy of the *Elements* in the Vatican library in Rome. This manuscript was translated and studied by the Danish classicist J. L. Heiberg, who published his version of the *Elements* in 1883–88. It is this 19th-century edition on which we base our modern knowledge of the *Elements*.

While his work earned its author the title the Geometer and shaped the nature of geometry for over 2,000 years, one of Euclid's original postulates bothered mathematicians for much of that period: his fifth postulate concerning parallel lines. Mathematicians wondered if it was independent of the other postulates. If one removed it or changed it, would one still have a geometry? In the middle of the 19th century, it was proven indeed to be independent, and variations of this postulate resulted in the discovery of new non-Euclidean geometries.

Name _____   Date _____

Questions and Investigations

Euclid of Alexandria

The following questions and investigations are intended to broaden a historical under-standing of the persons and issues examined. They should provoke thinking and guide further research on the subjects under discussion. In several instances, library resources may have to be consulted.

1. Locate Alexandria on a world map. What country is it found in today? Why would Euclid, a Greek, be living and working there?

   _____

   _____

   _____

2. What is an axiom? How does it differ from a postulate?

   _____

   _____

   _____

3. State Euclid's fifth postulate. Why did its contents cause mathematicians so much concern?

   _____

   _____

   _____

4. Name three other types of geometry besides Euclidean geometry.

   _____

   _____

   _____

5. Euclid's book the *Elements* was written in Greek and later translated into Arabic. Why was it translated into Arabic and not directly into Latin, the major Western language of the time?

   _____

   _____

   _____

Archimedes (287–212 B.C.)

Inventor and Mathematician

ARCHIMEDES PHILOSOPHE
Grec. Chap. 23.

About 287–212 B.C.

While the ancient Greek world gave birth to many creative scientists and thinkers, one man is recognized above the rest for his creative talents. He is Archimedes of Syracuse, born about 287 B.C. in the Greek city of Syracuse on the island of Sicily. His father was an astronomer, and it is believed that his family was related to the royal rulers of the city. Archimedes studied at the great Museum in Alexandria and was in contact with other outstanding scientists and mathematicians of his time. He spent most of his working life in Syracuse in the service of King Hieron. In this sense, he is one of the first known professional mathematicians to be in the employ of a government.

Archimedes was a great theoretical mathematician, experimenter, and inventor. In his work he revealed and explained many of the principles of basic physics we study today. One of his most useful inventions was a water pump based on the principle of a screw. By turning a handle and rotating the pump, water is forced to advance up a screw-type passage to a higher level. In Archimedes' time, such a pump was useful in irrigation and in draining mines and boats of unwanted water. These pumps are still used today in some parts of the world for irrigation purposes.

Many stories survive illustrating how Archimedes used his scientific knowledge to accomplish difficult tasks. One story relates how, with great difficulty, a large number of slaves dragged a ship ashore. Archimedes viewed this undertaking, then ordered the ship fully loaded with cargo and passengers. He attached a system of pulleys and ropes to it and then, while seated, single-handedly moved the ship farther up the shore employing the mechanical advantage of his pulley system. Once he remarked that he could move the world if given a proper lever and a fulcrum to place it on. Perhaps the most famous incident involving Archimedes' scientific talents is the "bath episode." King Hieron, the ruler of Syracuse, had a gold crown made and feared that his goldsmith had cheated him by mixing cheaper silver with the gold in the crown, thereby saving some gold for himself. The king sought Archimedes' help in solving this problem. Although he thought long and hard on this problem, the scientist could not resolve it. Then, while taking a bath, he noticed how his body displaced water. The water in the tub rose according to the density of the material submerged in it; thus a fixed amount of gold, when placed under water, would always displace the same amount of water regardless of its physical shape. Elated by this discovery, Archimedes ran home naked, shouting, "Eureka, eureka!" ["I have found it!"] This principle was used to test the gold in the crown, and the goldsmith was indeed found to be a cheat.

Despite his great talent for inventions, Archimedes considered such technical activities minor. For him, the only worthy activity was mathematics. He used an analytic approach, incorporating some of his mechanical techniques, in attempting to understand the properties of curves and solids. For example, he envisioned a spiral curve as being generated by a point moving through space. This dynamic concept of a curve allowed him to obtain solutions to the three classical problems of Greek concern: the duplication of a cube, the trisection of an angle, and the quadrature of a circle. However, Archimedes did not solve these problems by the required ruler and compass constructions. In investigating the properties of a circle, he inscribed and circumscribed regular polygons in and about a fixed circle. By increasing the number of sides of these polygons while computing their areas by a method of exhaustion, he estimated the area of the contained circle and, in turn, found a value for π. His value—$3\frac{10}{71} < \pi < 3\frac{1}{7}$—was very accurate for the time.

In general, Archimedes explored area and volume by theoretically breaking the geometric shapes down into simpler geometric forms for which the properties were known and then adding up these pieces of indivisibles to obtain a result. Such mathematical practices as exhaustion and the use of indivisibles employed a limiting concept and foreshadowed the later coming of calculus. It was through such experimentation that Archimedes arrived at correct formulas for the volume and surface area of a sphere. He was so fascinated by the discovery that both the volume and area of a sphere are exactly $\frac{2}{3}$ those of its circumscribing right circular cylinder that he asked a friend to have the figures of a sphere and cylinder carved on his tomb.

When in 212 B.C. Roman armies conquered Syracuse, Archimedes, absorbed in a geometric problem, ignored the command of a soldier and was killed. On his tomb were carved the pictures of a sphere and cylinder as he had requested.

Questions and Investigations

Archimedes of Syracuse

The following questions and investigations are intended to broaden a historical understanding of the persons and issues examined. They should provoke thinking and guide further research on the subjects under discussion. In several instances, library resources may have to be consulted.

1. Archimedes was born on the island of Sicily. Locate Sicily on a world map. What country is it part of today?

   _____

   _____

   _____

2. What scientific principle did Archimedes discover in his "bath episode"?

   _____

   _____

   _____

3. If a circle is drawn with a radius of 1 unit, what is the area of this circle? If squares were circumscribed about and inscribed in this circle, what would be the areas of these squares?

   _____

   _____

   _____

4. Obtain a five-decimal-point value for π from a calculator. Change Archimedes' values into decimal form and compare his accuracy with that of your calculator.

   _____

   _____

   _____

5. Given a right circular cylinder, a circular cone, and a hemisphere where the heights and radii of the cylinder and cone are equal to the value for the radius of the hemisphere, what is the relationship among the volumes of these three solids?

   _____

   _____

   _____

Liu Hui (ca. 250)

Mathematician of Ancient China and the Amazing Nine Chapters

About A.D. *250*

The most well-known mathematician in the Western world is the famous Greek, Euclid of Alexandria, and the best-known mathematical work is his book, the *Elements*. This association of Euclid and the *Elements* is easily recognized and praised as an important event in Western mathematical achievement. There is a similar association in the East of a great mathematician with an influential mathematical work. The mathematician is Liu Hui, who lived in 3rd-century China, and the mathematical work is the *Jiuzhang Suanshu* (*Nine Chapters on the Mathematical Art*).

Little is known about the life of Liu except that he was an official in the kingdom of Wei. China in this period of history was in civil and intellectual disarray. The mighty Han dynasty had collapsed, and its power had been seized by three generals, who each set up his own kingdom. These kingdoms went to war with each other. Eventually the kingdom of Wei emerged from the war victorious. Its ruler put his officials to work reviving traditional institutions and revising literary and scientific classics.

Liu revised the *Nine Chapters*, a collection of mathematics needed to run the empire. Each of its chapters considered a specific aspect of daily mathematics: Chapter 1, "Field Measurement"; Chapter 2, "Cereals" (deals with proportions); Chapter 3, "Distribution by Proportion"; Chapter 4, "What Width?" (deals with area and volume); Chapter 5, "Construction Calculations"; Chapter 6, "Fair Taxes"; Chapter 7,

"Excess and Deficiency" (discusses the solutions of linear equations); Chapter 8, "Rectangular Arrays" (provides for solutions of systems of equations); and Chapter 9, "*Gougu*" (employs the Pythagorean theorem to solve a variety of problems). The book consisted of a collection of 246 problems concerning the above topics together with their solution procedures. It was probably first compiled about 100 B.C. and represented the mathematics known and used in China up to that period.

Liu not only recopied the *Nine Chapters* but also expanded and strengthened its contents. He provided explanations and mathematical proofs for many of the procedures given and in some cases greatly improved the accuracy and scope of the mathematical results. For example, he obtained a better estimate for π by using circle division, whereby he systematically inscribed regular polygons in a given circle. Finally advancing to an n-gon of 192 sides, he estimated π to have a value of 3.141024—the most accurate value in the ancient world. He used dissection techniques and a concept of limits to investigate and verify formulas for area and volume. Liu extended the chapter on the right triangle by adding nine problems that involved more complicated solution procedures and foreshadowed a use of trigonometric ratios. Eventually, these nine problems were published as a separate mathematical classic called the *Sea Island Manual*.

Both the *Nine Chapters* and the *Sea Island Manual* set the standards and methods of Asian mathematics for the next thousand years. The contents of the *Nine Chapters* reveal the power of early Chinese mathematics. Some of its innovations include: use of a system of decimal fractions, computational use of negative numbers, solution procedures for systems of linear equations employing matrix techniques, accurate formulas for finding complicated areas and volumes, and a sophisticated knowledge and use of the Pythagorean theorem.

Liu is one of the first non-Greek mathematicians recognized to have developed and used methods of proof for his results. He is considered to be one of the greatest mathematicians of China.

Questions and Investigations

Liu Hui of the Wei Kingdom

The following questions and investigations are intended to broaden a historical understanding of the persons and issues examined. They should provoke thinking and guide further research on the subjects under discussion. In several instances, library resources may have to be consulted.

1. Liu Hui was a famous Chinese mathematician. Can you find the names of two other noted Chinese mathematicians and identify their accomplishments?

   _____

   _____

   _____

2. Do you think the development of mathematics in China was different from its development outside of China? Explain your answer.

   _____

   _____

   _____

3. The *Nine Chapters* contained problems involving volumes. What volumes would you think the early Chinese wished to compute?

   _____

   _____

   _____

4. The mathematical textbook *Nine Chapters* teaches its mathematics by the use of problems alone. Do you think this is a good method of teaching mathematics?

   _____

   _____

   _____

5. The contents of the *Nine Chapters* show that the Chinese of 100 B.C. could use negative numbers in their computations. Who are the people usually given credit for being the first to "invent" negative numbers?

   _____

   _____

   _____

Al-Khwarizmi (ca. 800–847)

Father of Algebra

About 800-847

Some of the greatest influences on European mathematics of the early Middle Ages came from outside Europe. One of these influences is the work of the Muslim mathematician popularly known as al-Khwarizmi. His full name was Abu Ja'far Muhammed ibn Musa al-Khwarizmi (Muhammed the father of Jofar and the son of Musa from Khwarizm), and although his family came from the city of Khwarizm near the Caspian Sea, it is believed that Muhammed was born near Baghdad in about the year 800.

During his reign, the Caliph al-Ma'mum established the Dar al-Hikma or House of Wisdom, in Baghdad, a kind of scientific academy, and invited the best scholars of the Islamic world to come to work at this facility. Al-Khwarizmi was appointed the chief astronomer and head of the library at this new House of Wisdom. The caliph requested him to write a popular book on the science of solving equations. Combining his knowledge of Greek and Hindu mathematics, al-Khwarizmi wrote *Al-Kitab al-Mukhtasar fi Hisab al-Jabr Wál-Muqabalah* (*The Compendious Book on Calculation by Completion and Balancing*), a clear account of the solution of simple algebraic equations. Al-Khwarizmi's systematic approach to solving equations depended on two processes: *al-jabr*, restoring or completing, which involves eliminating negative quantities on one side of an equation; and *muqabalah*, balancing, which allows for the combining of terms and the simplification of an equation. The book contained many practical examples of how to apply these techniques in solving equations and soon became a popular text within the Islamic empire, which extended to Spain and included the island of Sicily.

At a later period in his life, al-Khwarizmi wrote a book on the Hindu numerals and their computational schemes for the four basic operations of arithmetic. Although the original Arabic text has been lost and the book is only known through Latin translations, its title was probably *Kitab Hisab al-Adad al-Hindi* (*Treatise on Calculation with the Hindu Numerals*). This work introduced the Hindu numerals to the Islamic world. Eventually European scholars translated both of these works into Latin, and their contents had a great influence on the European mathematics scene. Solving equations by restoring and balancing became the science of *al-jabr*, a word whose spelling evolved into *algebra*, the term we recognize today. The Hindu numerals transmitted to Europe under al-Khwarizmi's influence became known as the Hindu-Arabic numerals. In Latin translation, al-Khwarizmi's name was changed into *algorizmi* and later *algorithm*, which today means a computational procedure.

In 842 Caliph al-Wathiq, al-Ma'mum's successor, became sick and summoned his astronomers/astrologers to cast his horoscope. Al-Khwarizmi and his colleagues did so and predicted that the caliph would live another 50 years. Unfortunately the caliph died 10 days later instead. Although his success in casting horoscopes was limited, al-Khwarizmi's influence on Western mathematics was important. This Muslim astronomer and mathematician died in the year 847.

Questions and Investigations

Al-Khwarizmi

The following questions and investigations are intended to broaden a historical understanding of the persons and issues examined. They should provoke thinking and guide further research on the subjects under discussion. In several instances, library resources may have to be consulted.

1. Many great Arabic mathematicians including al-Khwarizmi were astronomers. Why was astronomy so important to the Arab peoples?

   _____

   _____

   _____

2. If al-Khwarizmi were alive today, what nationality would he be?

   _____

   _____

   _____

3. The word *algebra* comes from the Arabic word *al-jabr*. Find two other modern scientific or mathematical terms whose origins come from Arabic.

   _____

   _____

   _____

4. Early ideas on algebra involved the processes of restoring and balancing. How do these two operations play a role in doing algebra?

   _____

   _____

   _____

5. How did the Arabs obtain a knowledge of the Hindu numerals before the people in Europe did?

   _____

   _____

   _____

Omar Khayyám (ca. 1044–1123)

Poet and Mathematician

About 1044–1123

An old Persian story tells how in the Middle Ages three boys named Nizam, Hasan, and Omar studied under a great teacher, the Imam Mowaffak of Naishapur. All three boys were good students and became the best of friends. Since the imam was so great a teacher, it was believed that some of his pupils would go on to achieve great wealth. The three friends promised that if one of them did become rich, he would share his wealth with the other two. As the years went by, Nizan became the chief adviser or vizier, to the Sultan Alp Arslan and indeed became a very rich man. He summoned his friends to fulfill his promise. Hasan requested a government post and received one. Omar desired neither a title nor a job but simply asked for some money that he might study mathematics and science. Impressed by Omar's humble modesty, the vizier granted him a pension to pursue his mathematical work.

Hasan went on to disgrace his post and was dismissed from the sultan's service and became a bandit. In contrast, Omar Khayyám became one of the greatest Islamic mathematicians of all time and a well-known poet. His most advanced work involved using geometric methods to solve cubic equations. By graphically intersecting a circle with a rectangular hyperbola, Omar could find positive roots for cubic equations. He systematically explored cubic equations and considered 19 types of them, which he categorized as either simple or compound depending on their form. In this work he ignored negative roots, as was the general practice of the time. Omar also knew and used the numerical arrangement of binomial coefficients later to be called Pascal's triangle (named after the French mathematician Blaise Pascal, who lived in the 17th century). Omar carried out a calendar reform for the caliph.

Omar was a talented geometer and undertook an investigation of Euclid's fifth postulate. He published his results in a work called *Discussion of the Difficulties in Euclid* in which he suggested the possibilities of alternate geometries, which would eventually be found in the 19th century. In many respects, Omar's approach to doing mathematics was very creative. This creativity was expressed in other ways: Omar was also a poet and wrote the *Rubáiyát*, a poem in four-line stanzas, which has remained famous down to the present day.

In his later years, Omar told one of his students that he wished his tomb to be located so that the wind could blow flower petals on it. He died in 1123. Some years after the death of his master, the student sought out Omar's tomb and found it covered with flower petals as the master had wished. Omar Khayyám is unique in that he achieved the status of being both a great mathematician and a famous poet.

Name _____ Date _____

Omar Khayyám

The following questions and investigations are intended to broaden a historical under-standing of the persons and issues examined. They should provoke thinking and guide further research on the subjects under discussion. In several instances, library resources may have to be consulted.

1. Omar found a method for solving a cubic equation. In Europe, who was the first mathe-matician credited with finding a method to solve cubic equations?

    _____

    _____

    _____

2. What is Pascal's triangle? Write out the five first lines of such a triangle.

    _____

    _____

    _____

3. Omar investigated the possibility of different geometries. How many different geome-tries can you name?

    _____

    _____

    _____

4. Omar lived between 1044 and 1123. What kind of mathematics was being done in Europe at this time?

    _____

    _____

    _____

5. Why could Omar ignore the negative roots of an equation?

    _____

    _____

    _____

Leonardo of Pisa (ca. 1175–1250)

The Mathematician of Many Names

Leonardo of Pisa (Fibonacci)
About 1175–1250

In the ancient and medieval worlds, merchants were often the carriers of new information and techniques. Thales while seeking trade in Egypt also found geometry, which he brought back to Greece where it was refined into a mathematical discipline. During the early Middle Ages, Italian cities such as Genoa, Pisa, Venice, and Florence became vital trade links to the Eastern world. Their merchant–adventurers traveled as far as China seeking exotic and valuable products for import into Europe. Once again, many of the wares brought westward were intellectual: knowledge of customs and practices, art, medicine, science, and mathematics.

One such merchant–adventurer altered the nature of European mathematics forever through his imports. Leonardo of Pisa left his native city as a young boy to accompany his father to Bougie on the coast of North Africa. In Bougie, the father was in charge of a Pisan trade warehouse and Leonardo lived in a world of traders and moneymen. He became known as Fibonacci, "son of Bonacci" (Filius Bonacci), and studied mathematics with a Moorish teacher. Later he traveled widely visiting Egypt, Syria, Greece, Sicily, and Constantinople and observed the trade and mathematics practices of the peoples he encountered. In particular Fibonacci learned the techniques of Arabic arithmetic and algebra.

Returning to Pisa in the year 1200, he settled down and two years later published a book titled *Liber Abaci* (*Book of Counting*). While most of the 15 chapters of this book were devoted to the mathematical problems of merchants such as exchanging money, its most dramatic feature was that it further introduced the Hindu-Arabic numerals and their computing schemes to the European audience. Some information on these numerals had reached Europe through the translated works of the Muslim mathematician al-Khwarizmi (ca. 800–847), but their use had not become popular. Most arithmetic calculations in Europe were still done mainly on an abacus and recorded in Roman numerals. Now a new system was available. The *Liber Abaci* also contained some interesting problems, one of which has become very famous:

> *How many pairs of rabbits can be produced from a single pair in a year if every month each pair begets a new pair which from the second month on becomes productive?*

The number of pairs of rabbits given as the answer to this problem form a very interesting sequence: 1, 1, 2, 3, 5, . . ., x, y, $x + y$, which later became known as the Fibonacci sequence and has been recognized in some unusual places and situations.

In 1220 Fibonacci wrote *Practica Geometriae* (*Practical Geometry*), an applied geometry book, that included work on surveying, methods for find-ing square and cube roots, and some considerations in algebra and geometry. His reputation as a skilled mathematician grew. Attracted by this reputation, Emperor Frederick II, a patron of learning, invited Fibonacci to participate in a mathematical contest he was sponsoring. Three difficult problems were made up by John of Palermo, a mathematician employed by the emperor. No one was able to answer the contest questions correctly except Fibonacci, who emerged the winner. The third of these challenging questions involved an indeterminate equation, a subject in which Fibonacci had a strong interest. This interest was expressed in his *Liber Quadratorum* (*Book of Squares*), written in 1225. Its subject concerned finding solutions for indeterminate equations of the second degree. He wrote several other books, all of which were recognized for their brilliant mathematical exposition.

Fibonacci sometimes signed his work "Leonardo Bigollo." In the Italian of the time, *bigollo* could mean either "traveler" or "blockhead." It would seem that both could apply, as he was certainly a great traveler but also was ridiculed as a blockhead for his interest in the strange new numbers from the East. Whether he was Leonardo of Pisa, Fibonacci, or Leonardo Bigollo, he remains the greatest European mathematician of his time.

Name _____   Date _____

Leonardo of Pisa

The following questions and investigations are intended to broaden a historical under-standing of the persons and issues examined. They should provoke thinking and guide further research on the subjects under discussion. In several instances, library resources may have to be consulted.

1. On a world map, locate the cities of Pisa and Bougie. In what countries are they found today?

   _____

   _____

   _____

2. Leonardo helped to introduce the Hindu-Arabic numerals into Europe and replace the use of Roman numerals. Why are the Hindu-Arabic numerals better than the Roman numerals?

   _____

   _____

   _____

3. Find out some further information about Fibonacci numbers.

   _____

   _____

   _____

4. What is an indeterminate equation?

   _____

   _____

   _____

5. Find a historical method for approximating the cube root of a number. Use this method to find $\sqrt[3]{54}$ and check your answer with a calculator.

   _____

   _____

   _____

Niccolò Tartaglia (ca. 1499–1557)

A Self-Taught Mathematician of the Renaissance

LA PRIMA PARTE DEL
GENERAL TRATTATO DI NV‚
MERI, ET MISVRE DI NICOLO TARTAGLIA,

NELLAQVALE IN DIECISETTE
LIBRI SI DICHIARA TVTTI GLI ATTI OPERATIVJ,
PRATICHE, ET REGOLE NECESSARIE NON SOLA-
mente in tutta l'arte negotiaria, & mercantile, ma anchor in ogni altra
arte, scientia, ouer disciplina, doue interuenghi il calculo.

MALIGNITA'

NOIAR NON PVO

A' FORTEZZA

CON LI SVOI PRIVILEGII.

In Vinegia per Curtio Troiano dei Nauò.
M D LV I.

About 1499–1557

One of the first comprehensive mathematics books published during the historical period known as the Renaissance was the *Summa de Arithmetica Geometria Proportioni et Proportionalita*. It was written by a priest, Luca Pacioli (ca. 1445–1517), in 1494. The *Summa* contained all of the mathematics of the time and ended by stating that the solution for a cubic equation was impossible. This statement gave a challenge to Italian mathematicians.

In about 1515, Scipione del Ferro (1465–1526), a professor of mathematics at the University of Bologna, solved one form of the cubic equation, $x^3 + ax = b$. On his deathbed, he taught his method to a student, Antonio Maria Fior (ca. 1506–?), who took great pride in this secret, powerful mathematical knowledge. Fior learned that a reckoning master, Niccolò Tartaglia, also claimed to have solved a form of the cubic equation, $x^3 + px^2 = q$. Fior challenged Tartaglia to a public contest on solving cubic equations. Tartaglia won this contest easily, thus identifying himself as an expert in solving cubic equations.

Tartaglia was one of the greatest Italian mathematicians of the 16th century. Tartaglia was a nickname; his actual name was Niccolò Fontana, and he was also called Niccolò of Brescia. Tartaglia was born of poor parents in the northern Italian city of Brescia about the year 1499. In 1512 French armies sacked Brescia and killed many of its inhabitants. Tartaglia's father was killed in this raid, and Tartaglia himself was seriously wounded in the jaw and

Learning Activities from the History of Mathematics

mouth. His mother nursed him back to health, but his wounds and scars impaired his speech so that he stuttered. This impediment earned him the cruel nickname the Stammerer—in Italian, *Tartaglia*. His fatherless family was now so poor that his mother only had enough money to send him to school for 15 days. He did, however, manage to obtain a book from which he taught himself to read and write. Legend also tells how, unable to afford paper to write on, Tartaglia used the tombstones in a graveyard as slates. Although self-taught, he overcame the difficulties of his early life to become a respected reckoning master, a teacher of science and mathematics. His work with cubic equations attracted great attention within the mathematics community of Italy.

Tartaglia was befriended by another mathematician, Girolamo Cardano (1501–1576), who sought his secrets for solving cubic equations. Cardano begged the solution from Tartaglia, pledging to keep this information secret. Finally in 1539,

Tartaglia gave in and told Cardano his mathematical secret. In 1545, Cardano published an algebra book titled *Ars Magna* (*The Great Art*) in which he revealed Tartaglia's solution procedure for the cubic equation. Tartaglia accused Cardano of copying from him, and a dispute began that lasted for many years as to who was the real discoverer of the solutions procedure for the cubic equation.

This controversy was yet another unhappiness in the life of Tartaglia, but it did not stop his career as a great mathematician. He went on to research the mathematics of artillery trajectories and wrote the first book on this subject, *Nova Scientia* (*The New Science*) in 1537, and published a two-volume book on arithmetic, plus books on Euclid and Archimedes. Rather than being ashamed of his nickname the Stammerer, he proudly used it for all his works so that for generations to come people would know of Tartaglia, the great mathematician. He died in 1557.

Questions and Investigations

Niccolò Tartaglia

The following questions and investigations are intended to broaden a historical under-standing of the persons and issues examined. They should provoke thinking and guide further research on the subjects under discussion. In several instances, library resources may have to be consulted.

1. The great mathematics book written by Luca Pacioli in 1494 was popularly called the *Summa*, a Latin word. What does *Summa* mean?

   _____

   _____

   _____

2. By profession Niccolò Tartaglia was a reckoning master. What did reckoning masters do?

   _____

   _____

   _____

3. Research the life of Cardano. What were some of his accomplishments? Was he a good mathematician?

   _____

   _____

   _____

4. Tartaglia studied the paths of artillery shells. What other Italian mathematician studied the paths of objects moving through space?

   _____

   _____

   _____

5. On a map of Italy, locate the city of Brescia, birthplace of Tartaglia.

   _____

   _____

   _____

François Viète (1540–1603)

"To Leave No Problem Unsolved"

1540–1603

François Viète was a gifted amateur mathematician. By profession he was a lawyer and served as a member of the French parliament. Viète wrote a number of books on algebra, geometry, and trigonometry. In one of these books he explained how the six trigonometric functions could be used to solve problems involving plane and spherical triangles, a new theory for western Europe.

On at least two occasions Viète's mathematical ability was called to the service of his country. When France was at war with Spain, Viète successfully figured out the Spanish code that contained several hundred characters. For two years France used this special knowledge to read Spain's secret messages to great advantage. So disturbed was the Spanish king, Philip II, at this situation that he complained to the pope that the French must be using witchcraft against him. On another occasion the ambassador from Holland boasted to the French king Henry IV that the Dutch mathematician Adrianus Romanus (1561–1615) had found a 45th-degree equation that no Frenchman could solve. Viète was summoned. He studied the equation for a few minutes and, through use of his knowledge of trigonometry, found 2 roots. Later he went on to find 21 more. In turn Viète offered a problem for the Dutchman Romanus. The Dutch mathematician could not solve it, and when he saw Viète's solution he became the Frenchman's adamant admirer and friend.

Photo courtesy of the New York Public Library

When working on a mathematical problem, Viète would stay in his room for days trying to find a solution. Such an effort allowed him to estimate the value of π accurately to nine decimal places. However, Viète's most notable contribution to the mathematics of his time was the development of a symbolic algebra. In writing equations he used vowels to represent unknown quantities and consonants to represent known quantities. This theory of algebra as the art of manipulatory symbols was advanced in his book *In Artem*, published in 1579. Viète ended this book by quoting his motto, "To leave no problem unsolved," a saying that guided much of his life's work. Viète died in 1603. Today he is recognized as the greatest French mathematician of the 16th century and one of the founders of algebra.

Name _____   Date _____

François Viète

The following questions and investigations are intended to broaden a historical understanding of the persons and issues examined. They should provoke thinking and guide further research on the subjects under discussion. In several instances, library resources may have to be consulted.

1. What was the name of the war between France and Spain in which Viète's knowledge of codes was important?

    _____

    _____

    _____

2. Who was the ruler of England at the time Viète lived?

    _____

    _____

    _____

3. François Viète was a great French mathematician. Name three other French mathematicians who lived before the 18th century.

    _____

    _____

    _____

4. How many solutions can a 45th-degree equation have? Do they all have to be different?

    _____

    _____

    _____

5. How were algebra problems written before the use of symbols?

    _____

    _____

    _____

René Descartes (1596–1650)

"I Think, Therefore, I Am."

1596–1650

When Johannes Kepler discovered his three laws of planetary motion, he showed how the planets moved through the heavens and demonstrated that mathematics could be used to unravel the secrets of nature. His work encouraged other scientists and philosophers to view nature as a vast "machine" that worked according to definite laws or rules which could be isolated and studied. Perhaps the most successful scientist–philosopher to attempt this feat was the Frenchman René Descartes.

Descartes was born in 1596 near the city of Tours. As a young child he was very sickly, and his parents allowed him to remain in bed late through the morning. He kept this habit throughout his life and used this leisure time in bed to think and write. Descartes inherited his mother's wealth, so he did not have to work to support himself. He graduated from the university with a law degree but did not practice law. Instead he traveled to Paris, where he enjoyed the good life. In Paris he associated with famous scientists and became interested in the study of mathematics and philosophy.

In 1617 Descartes joined the army as a gentleman soldier, first serving in the forces of Prince Maurice of Holland and later in the army of the duke of Bavaria. Still of a weak physical nature, Descartes disliked the cold. Once while in winter quarters in Bavaria, he escaped the cold by locking himself in a closed, overheated room and as a result fell into a feverish sleep. During this sleep he had three dreams in which his future career as a mathematician and philosopher was revealed to him. Descartes emerged from this experience proclaiming that he had discovered a marvelous new science; however, it would be many years before the nature of this science became known.

Descartes left military service in 1622 and traveled around Europe for the next five years, finally settling in Holland. Here he undertook the scientific experimentation and writings that were to make him famous. In 1633 he proposed a theory on the motion of planets. He believed that all space was filled with tiny globules of matter that formed an ether. The sun in its violence caused a whirlpool or vortex in this ether, and the vortex swept the planets about the sun in their orbits. This theory was debated for many years until Isaac Newton (1642–1727) offered another theory based on the principle of gravitation.

Descartes also worked on problems in physics, biology, optics, physiology, philosophy, and theology as well as mathematics. During his metaphysical contemplation, he even questioned his own existence but soon resolved the matter by noting that if he doubted his existence, he was involved in the activity of thought, and the action of thought indicated existence. Thus emerged his famous quotation: "I think, therefore I am."

In 1637 Descartes published his greatest work, the *Discourse*, which explained his scientific approach to research. Attached to the *Discourse*

were three essays, one of which, *La Géométrie* (*Geometry*), was to have a great effect on mathematical thinking. *La Geometry* was divided into three sections: The first combined methods of algebra with geometry, allowing for the use of equations to represent curves; the second provided methods for analytically constructing tangents to given curves; and the third offered solution methods for equations beyond the second degree. By "inventing" analytic geometry, Descartes provided a valuable tool for use in the scientific revolution of the 17th century. Unfortunately his writing was difficult to read, and many implications remained obscure until the work was rewritten by the Dutch mathematician Frans van Schooten and republished in Latin in 1649. This book was reprinted three more times in the 17th century (1659–61, 1683, and 1693) and became a major reference for future generations of philosophers and scientists.

In 1649 Descartes was invited to Sweden by Queen Christiana to serve as her philosophy teacher and to help establish a scientific academy in the country. A robust woman, the queen chose to receive her lessons at five o'clock in the morning in an unheated library. Although he was used to late rising and hated the cold, Descartes did what the queen asked; after all, she was the monarch. These hardships took their toll on the mathematician–philosopher: he caught pneumonia and died in 1650. He was first buried in Sweden, then 17 years later reburied in Paris as a national hero.

Questions and Investigations

René Descartes

The following questions and investigations are intended to broaden a historical under-standing of the persons and issues examined. They should provoke thinking and guide further research on the subjects under discussion. In several instances, library resources may have to be consulted.

1. Descartes was a participant in the scientific revolution of the 17th century. What were some of the scientific accomplishments of this revolution?

   _____

   _____

   _____

2. How did analytic geometry provide a valuable tool for scientists?

   _____

   _____

   _____

3. Was Descartes' *La Geometry* translated into Latin?

   _____

   _____

   _____

4. Discuss Descartes' theory of how planets move. On what basis could he have thought up such a theory?

   _____

   _____

   _____

5. Besides translating Descartes' book, what else did the Dutch mathematician Frans van Schooten do?

   _____

   _____

   _____

Johannes Kepler (1571–1630)

The Seeker of Celestial Harmony

1571–1630

For over a thousand years Western Europe held to a model of the universe based on simplicity and harmony. The visible planets, sun and moon included, moved around the earth in a series of concentric circles. An earth-centered universe was supported by the Bible and advocated by the power of the Catholic Church.

In 1543 the Polish monk and university professor Nicolaus Copernicus (1473–1543) published a theory that placed the sun at the center of the universe. The earth merely became another planet revolving in a circular orbit around the sun. This solar-centric theory attracted other scientists and mathematicians of the time. One scientist who attempted to extend and refine this theory was the German astronomer Johannes Kepler.

Kepler was born in 1571 into a poor family. His father was a mercenary soldier, and his mother was later accused of being a witch. When Johannes was four years old he caught smallpox, which left him with poor eyesight and disabled hands for the rest of his life. His schooling was erratic, but his potential attracted the attention of the duke of Württemberg, who paid for his attendance at the university. Kepler studied to become a Lutheran minister. In his graduation dissertation he discussed the principle of a sun-centered universe, a concept against Church teaching, and was subsequently dismissed from the university. He then embarked on an unsuccessful university teaching career and a lifelong research quest in mathematics and astronomy to

Photo courtesy of The Granger Collection

44

unravel the divine plan for the universe. Unfortunately his life was still beset with difficulties. Kepler's favorite child died of smallpox and his wife went mad and also died. After carefully considering 11 possible mates, he chose another wife.

Kepler believed that "perfect knowledge is always mathematical" and sought to understand the orbits of the planets in terms of mathematics. He speculated that the planets moved in circular orbits, the radii of which were determined by the relationship of a set of regular polyhedra around which spheres could be circumscribed. This theory depended heavily on Pythagorean number mysticism. It did *not* work.

In 1601 Kepler became the assistant of the most famous astronomer in Europe, the Dane Tycho Brahe (1546–1601). Brahe was noted for his very accurate astronomical measurements. During a lifetime of working in astronomy, he had acquired an enormous amount of data. After a brief association, Tycho Brahe died and Kepler inherited these valuable data. Now Kepler had facts upon which to justify his planetary theories. He still believed that the planets orbited the sun along a smooth path that was not quite circular—perhaps it was egg-shaped. Calculating such an orbit for the planet Mars, Kepler compared his predicted positions with those observed by Brahe. This theory did not work either. Finally he tried an orbit in the shape of an ellipse. The orbit matched the observed data. Kepler then assumed the other planets followed similar orbits and again checked this theory against his data. It

worked! Johannes Kepler had solved the mystery of how planets revolved about the sun. Eight years of calculations and conjectures had produced two laws:

1. The planets move about the sun in elliptical paths with the sun at one focus of the described ellipse.
2. The radius vector joining a planet to the sun sweeps over equal areas in equal time periods.

Ten more years of work produced a third law:

3. The square of the period for one revolution of a planet through its orbit is proportional to the cube of the elliptical orbit's semimajor axis.

Kepler's three laws stand as a monumental discovery for the times and a testimony to the power of persistence. In all, he had worked 18 years to arrive at these laws.

Kepler also made notable discoveries about the geometry of polyhedra and computed the volumes of 92 solids of revolution that might serve as wine casks. In problem-solving, he often used geometrical intuition by dividing a geometric form into simpler shapes and, by a limiting process of exhaustion, deriving properties of the parent form. Throughout his life money was a problem, and he was forced to cast horoscopes to support his family. Kepler experienced an untimely death in 1630 while seeking out some money that was owed to him.

Name _____ Date _____

Johannes Kepler

The following questions and investigations are intended to broaden a historical understanding of the persons and issues examined. They should provoke thinking and guide further research on the subjects under discussion. In several instances, library resources may have to be consulted.

1. Before the time of Copernicus, whose theory did people follow regarding the movements of the planets?

   _____

   _____

   _____

2. What was the Copernican theory of the universe?

   _____

   _____

   _____

3. Tycho Brahe was a very interesting character in the history of science. Research his life and find five interesting facts concerning him.

   _____

   _____

   _____

4. According to Kepler's laws, do the planets travel around the sun at a constant speed? Justify your answer.

   _____

   _____

   _____

5. Kepler discovered star polygons. What is a star polygon?

   _____

   _____

   _____

Isaac Newton (1642–1727)

Conqueror of Nature's Secrets

1642–1727

Isaac Newton was born in 1642, the same year Galileo Galilei died. As a son in an English farming family of modest means, he would have been destined to a life as a farmer had he not shown some talent for inventing when he was a small boy. He experimented with many devices. Once he made a tiny mill powered by mice for grinding grain. On another occasion he frightened local villagers by flying kites at night with lanterns attached to them; the villagers thought comets were going to crash into the earth. He did not do well in school and was considered a poor student.

In 1661 Newton entered Trinity College, Cambridge, and there his life truly changed. He studied for a law degree but soon began to read books by mathematicians such as Euclid, Kepler, Viète, and Descartes and became very interested in mathematics. Eventually his interest in law disappeared and he embarked on serious studies and experimentation in mathematics, physics, astronomy, theology, and alchemy. In particular he was interested in "subjecting the phenomena of Nature to the laws of mathematics."

The bubonic plague hit England in 1665, killing thousands of people. Cambridge University closed for two years and sent its students home. Isaac Newton returned to his country home and immersed himself in mathematical studies. It was during this period that he devised his method of fluxions, the differential calculus. Returning to Cambridge in 1667, Newton began earnest work in optics. He discovered the composition of white light and developed a theory of light based on a concept of particles. He believed that light was formed by collections of small corpuscles or particles and that the difference in the color of light as seen when light passes through a glass prism is due to the different velocities at which light particles move after passing through the glass. Newton's theory came under attack from the scientific community, and the opposition he encountered made him reluctant to release future theories to the public.

In 1669 his professor Isaac Barrow (1630–1677) resigned his teaching post and nominated Newton as his successor. Thus Newton became a professor of mathematics at Trinity College. He continued his experimentations and made friends with the noted astronomer Edmund Halley (1656–1742). By 1685 Newton had completed his major work, *Philosophiae Naturalis Principia Mathematica*, commonly referred to as the *Principia*. In this book he introduced a theory of gravitation that explained why the planets travel in elliptical orbits and, in doing so, completed the scientific picture Kepler had drawn of the solar system. Also contained within the *Principia* were three principal laws of motion, the most important being that a moving body exerts a force directly proportional to the product of its mass and the acceleration it is experiencing. These laws would revolutionize the study of dynamics. In developing these theories Newton used his principles of fluxions, which today we know as the calculus. Under prodding from his friend Halley, Newton published the *Principia* in 1687. The cost of the project was borne by Halley.

Newton's work was praised throughout Europe, and he was openly acknowledged as being one of the greatest scientists and natural philosophers of his time. However, he was still embroiled in controversy. The French upheld Descartes' theory of vortices against Newton's principles of gravity. A German, Gottfried Wilhelm Leibniz (1646–1716), released his own theory of the calculus, starting the dispute as to who "invented" the calculus first, Leibniz or Newton. This latter controversy plagued Newton for the rest of his life. Although he had recorded his theory of fluxions in 1671 in a work entitled *The Method of Fluxions*, it was not published until 1736; and the *Principia*, in which he used his principles of fluxions, had not appeared until 1687.

Newton suffered a mental breakdown in 1692 due, some felt, to his alchemy experiments with arsenic. He recovered and in 1696 became master of the British mint. Although involved in public service for the rest of his life, he remained a highly respected scientist. In 1705 he was honored by being made a knight of the British Empire for his contributions to British science. Newton died in 1727. The essence of Newton's work was captured poetically by Alexander Pope in these lines:

> *Nature and Nature's laws lay hid in night;*
> *God said, "Let Newton be," and all was light.*

Name _____ Date _____

Isaac Newton

The following questions and investigations are intended to broaden a historical understanding of the persons and issues examined. They should provoke thinking and guide
further research on the subjects under discussion. In several instances, library resources may
have to be consulted.

1. What was the bubonic plague, and how did it affect Europe in the time of Newton?

   _____

   _____

   _____

2. There is a famous story about Newton and an apple. What is the story?

   _____

   _____

   _____

3. What are Newton's three laws of motion?

   _____

   _____

   _____

4. Name three other British mathematicians who lived in Newton's time; describe their
   work.

   _____

   _____

   _____

5. Newton developed two important optical instruments. What were they?

   _____

   _____

   _____

Gottfried Wilhelm Leibniz (1646–1716)

The Versatile Genius

1646–1716

Gottfried Wilhelm Leibniz was the son of a German university professor. Young Gottfried exhibited his talent for learning quite early. By the time he was eight years old he had learned Latin; by twelve he knew Greek. Much of this knowledge was obtained through self-study by reading the books in his father's library. He entered the university when he was fifteen years old, embarking on a study of law, but his interests were broad, so he also undertook studies in philosophy, theology, and mathematics. He eventually obtained a law degree and began work as a diplomat, an occupation he would pursue for the rest of his life.

In 1672 a diplomatic mission brought Leibniz to Paris, which at that time was the intellectual center of the Western world. In Paris, Leibniz was befriended by the great Dutch mathematician and scientist Christiaan Huygens (1629–1695), who was attracted by the young German's keen intellect. Under the direction of Huygens, Leibniz began serious studies in mathematics and his genius blossomed in the subject. His Paris years, from 1672 to 1676, were mathematically his most productive. It was during this period that Leibniz developed his principles for calculus. He continually sought a universal mathematics-like language that could be used to obtain solutions for any scientific problem. In reality, he was formulating a system of deductive logic.

Throughout his mathematical work, Leibniz frequently introduced and standardized mathematical notation and terms. For example, he is responsible for the decimal point symbol as we know it and our present system of writing numerical exponents. He was also the first person to introduce the term *function* into mathematics. He was an equally keen inventor and experimenter as he was a theorist. He built a gear-driven computing machine that could perform the four basic operations of arithmetic. Commenting on the need for such a device, he noted, "It is unworthy of excellent men to lose hours like slaves in the labor of calculation." His machine was the most advanced computing device of its time. Leibniz presented it to the British Royal Society in 1673 and, as a result, was elected a member of that prestigious body. Not all of his inventions were so grand; he also designed a wagon wheel that could travel through mud and a nail that could secure wood more firmly than the nails then in use.

In 1684 Leibniz published his theories of calculus. Isaac Newton, although accomplished in the subject, did not publish his own work reflecting his knowledge of the subject until 1687. A bitter controversy began as to who "invented" the calculus first. It divided the mathematical community into two factions: supporters of Leibniz's claim to priority and those who favored Newton. The British Royal Society voted in support of Newton, its president. Nationalistic pride was at stake, a pride that was particularly strong in Great Britain. For the next hundred years, mathematicians on the Continent used the analytically derived calculus of Leib-

niz, while those of the British Isles preferred the geometrically based calculus of Newton. This split and its resulting isolation proved particularly detrimental to the development of British mathematics over this period.

Even in his diplomatic work Leibniz was innovative and creative. A deeply religious man, he was disturbed by the division of the Christian Church and unsuccessfully tried to reunite it. He was fascinated by the religions and cultures of the East and extended his linguistic abilities to include Sanskrit. He studied the *I Ching*, the classical book of Chinese fortune-telling, and in its primary mystical figures, the trigrams, saw an application of binary arithmetic. Associating the Chinese interest in the duality of nature with Christian theology, Leibniz devised a theory whereby God was represented by the number 1 and the void by 0 and, by combining these two numbers in a binary arithmetic, demonstrated how creation took place. While this numerical analogy was similar to Chinese traditional beliefs, it did not convert the Chinese people to Christianity as Leibniz had wished.

Leibniz led an extremely productive and varied life. Many historians feel that he would have been an even greater mathematician had he only concentrated more on mathematics. Perhaps this is true, but then he would not have been such an interesting and unusual person. When Leibniz died in 1716 only his secretary attended the funeral.

Questions and Investigations

Gottfried Wilhelm Leibniz

The following questions and investigations are intended to broaden a historical under-standing of the persons and issues examined. They should provoke thinking and guide further research on the subjects under discussion. In several instances, library resources may have to be consulted.

1. Isn't it strange that both Newton and Leibniz "invented" calculus at about the same time? What conditions helped this coincidence come about?

    _____

    _____

    _____

2. What was the British Royal Society and what did it do?

    _____

    _____

    _____

3. Sanskrit is a language usually used in what country?

    _____

    _____

    _____

4. What were some of the scientific accomplishments of Christiaan Huygens?

    _____

    _____

    _____

5. Find the decimal equivalent of the binary number 101101.

    _____

    _____

    _____

Sophie Germain (1776–1831)

The Mysterious M. Le Blanc

1776–1831

In 1801 when *Arithmetical Investigations*, the great work of Carl Friedrich Gauss (1777–1855) on number theory, first appeared, it attracted correspondence for its author. Other members of the mathematical community working in number theory now sought the advice and assistance of Gauss. One such letter, which contained some very interesting findings, was signed simply M. Le Blanc, Polytechnique student. Gauss was deeply impressed with the quality of the work and amazed that an unknown student from the French École Polytechnique could produce work of such standards. He began a correspondence with the mysterious Monsieur Le Blanc (Mr. White) that lasted several years.

Another contemporary mathematician Joseph Louis Lagrange (1736–1813) also had encountered Monsieur Le Blanc but on a more personal, revealing basis. Lagrange at this time was the instructor of mathematical analysis at the École Polytechnique in Paris, the famous French institution for the training of mathematicians and scientists. As was the custom, at the end of each term students at the Polytechnique submitted reports to their professors commenting on the studies completed and presenting their own findings and conclusions on the subjects in question. Lagrange received one such report from M. Le Blanc and was so impressed by the mathematics accomplished that he personally sought out the author to congratulate him on the excellent caliber of his work. Imagine the great Lagrange's surprise when he discovered that Monsieur Le Blanc was really a woman, Sophie Germain, who due to the prohibition of women studying at the Polytechnique, was forced to assume a male pseudonym. Germain could not even attend Legrange's lectures; she absorbed his teaching through self-study from a set of notes. This situation was typical of the period—women could not formally study higher mathematics no matter how bright or talented they were. In fact, Germain had taught herself Latin, Greek, and mathematics from books in the library of her father, a well-to-do merchant. Now she feared that if she wrote to Lagrange under her own name, he would ignore the correspondence, realizing she was a woman; thus, she resorted to deception. She later used this same ruse on Gauss. Lagrange was taken with her apparent talent and interest in mathematics. He praised her as a promising young mathematician of the future and openly introduced her to other leading French scientists. Germain began a broader scientific correspondence among these new acquaintances.

In a similar manner, still fearful of her feminine status in the world of mathematics, she began a correspondence with Gauss as M. Le Blanc. It was not until the dramatic events of 1806 that Gauss would learn the true identity of his talented correspondent. In that year, Napoleon's troops occupied the German state of Brunswick and attacked the city of Hanover, home of Gauss. Germain, worried about Gauss's well-being, requested the commanding French officer, a personal friend, to provide for the mathematician's safety, which he did. Gauss was puzzled as to the identity of his benefactress, one Mademoiselle Sophie Germain. What was her interest in him? The mystery was solved in later correspondence with M. Le Blanc when Germain finally admitted her true identity.

Germain continued her work in number theory and also achieved recognition for accomplishments in the field of applied mathematics, where she investigated problems on the transmission of sound and the theory of vibrations. In particular she won a top prize from the French Academy of Science in 1816 for her mathematical theories explaining Chladni figures, which are displayed when a layer of sand is placed on vibrating plates. The phenomenon was first observed and studied by the German physicist Ernst Chladni (1756–1827).

Gauss and Germain never met personally. In 1831 Gauss arranged for Germain to receive an honorary doctorate in science from the University of Göttingen in recognition of her work in mathematics. For a woman this was an unheard-of honor. Unfortunately Germain died of cancer before receiving the degree. Her story testifies to the conditions of prejudice and hardship experienced by women scientists and mathematicians for many years. Only recently have the scientific accomplishments and contributions of women been openly acknowledged and more fully appreciated.

Questions and Investigations

Sophie Germain

The following questions and investigations are intended to broaden a historical understanding of the persons and issues examined. They should provoke thinking and guide further research on the subjects under discussion. In several instances, library resources may have to be consulted.

1. Why do you think women were discouraged from studying mathematics in the time of Sophie Germain?

   _____

   _____

   _____

2. Do you feel that once Germain's mathematical talent became known, she received the recognition she deserved?

   _____

   _____

   _____

3. Name three other famous women mathematicians and their accomplishments.

   _____

   _____

   _____

4. Research the topic of Chladni figures and draw sketches of them.

   _____

   _____

   _____

5. Who might have been some of the French scientists Lagrange introduced Germain to?

   _____

   _____

   _____

Carl Friedrich Gauss (1777–1855)

The Prince of Mathematics

1777–1855

After the discovery of calculus, the body of mathematical knowledge increased very rapidly. Before Newton's time, the skill of a mathematician could span all mathematical activities, but after the 18th century this became increasingly difficult and by the 19th century, utterly impossible. A mathematician singled out as being the "last complete mathematician," that is, one who could contribute to all the fields of mathematics known in his time, was Carl Friedrich Gauss. Gauss was born in 1777 in Brunswick, Germany, into a poor and uneducated family. By the age of three he was recognized as a prodigy in mathematics, a "wonder child" who could easily correct the mathematical mistakes of his elders. As a schoolboy at age ten he was given the busywork task of computing the sum of the first hundred natural numbers and amazed his schoolmasters by obtaining the correct answer within a few minutes. He had recognized a pattern in the numbers and used it to deduce the fact that the sum of the first n natural numbers is given by the expression $n(n+1)/2$.

The genius of young Gauss was recognized by the local duke of Brunswick, who became his patron for life, sending him to the university and later supporting his research activities. Despite his obvious talent in mathematics, Gauss entered the University of Göttingen intending to study philology, the science of languages. But on March 30, 1796, he made a discovery that so impressed him with the beauty and power of mathematics that he decided to make it his life's career. Since ancient times the constructibility of regular polygons had been an open question: "Which regular polygons can be constructed using only a straightedge and compass?" Gauss proved that if $p = 2^{2^n} + 1$ is a prime number for a natural number n, then the p-gon is constructible. In 1801 he published his book on number theory, *Arithmetical Investigations*.

For Gauss "mathematics was the queen of the sciences, and the theory of numbers was the queen of mathematics." Another of his early accomplishments was the invention of the method of least squares for finding the best value for a sequence of measurements of the same quantity. He went on to do pioneering work in theoretical astronomy, the study of electromagnetism, complex number theory, probability, and the study of special geometrical surfaces. His work on surfaces resulted in the branch of mathematics we now call differential geometry. Gauss had both a geometry named after him as well as a probability distribution. In 1807 he assumed the position of director of the observatory at Göttingen and kept this position until his death in 1855.

Gauss was clearly recognized as the greatest mathematician of the 19th century. He has since been ranked along with Newton and Archimedes as one of the three greatest mathematicians of all time. Perhaps the most appropriate honorary title bestowed upon him was the one given by the king of Hanover, who called Gauss the Prince of Mathematics, a position he has retained over the years.

Name _____ Date _____

Carl Friedrich Gauss

The following questions and investigations are intended to broaden a historical understanding of the persons and issues examined. They should provoke thinking and guide further research on the subjects under discussion. In several instances, library resources may have to be consulted.

1. Find the sum of the first 100 even integers.

   _____

   _____

   _____

2. Using the rule discovered by Gauss, list the first five constructible regular polygons.

   _____

   _____

   _____

3. Which regular polygons were the ancient Greeks able to construct using only a ruler and compass?

   _____

   _____

   _____

4. In which branch of physics does the name Gauss serve as a unit of measure?

   _____

   _____

   _____

5. What is the common name for the geometry that Gauss helped to invent? What other mathematicians' names are usually associated with this geometry?

   _____

   _____

   _____

Charles Babbage (1792–1871)

The Father of Modern Computing

1792–1871

Charles Babbage was born in 1792 into a wealthy British family. As a child he was privately educated and entered Cambridge University in 1810. At the university, he was disappointed at the quality of British mathematics in comparison with what was taught on the Continent. He set about to correct this situation, joining with two other concerned students: George Peacock (1791–1858), who would go on to become "the Euclid of algebra," and John Herschel (1792–1871), later to become a noted astronomer. Among the calculus reforms the trio promoted was the adoption of Leibniz's differential notation in place of that established by Newton—a policy that did not make them popular with their British colleagues.

After graduation from Cambridge, Babbage became involved in a great variety of activities to improve British mathematics. He criticized the unprogressive nature of British scientific societies and set about establishing new ones. He helped found the Astronomical Society in 1820 and later, in 1834, the Statistical Society of London. A prolific and varied researcher, Babbage was interested in cryptography, astronomy, geophysics, meteorology, actuarial science, and improved lighthouse technology.

Babbage's concern with meteorology led him to investigate the use of a tree's rings as a measure of weather conditions, and his pioneering work in the study of manufacturing processes provided a basis for the modern study of operations research.

Photo courtesy of the Library of Congress

Learning Activities from the History of Mathematics

Above all, he was fascinated by machines and the possibility of employing machines to simplify numerical computations.

Using a mathematical method of finite differences, Babbage compiled a table of eight-place logarithms for the first 108,000 natural numbers. It is one of the most accurate mathematical tables ever made. He then sought to design an "engine" or computer that could use a method of finite differences to calculate functions. This "difference engine" was decimal in nature and performed its operations by using gears. Babbage felt strongly that national governments should support scientific activities and obtained funding from the British government to develop the difference engine. Unfortunately the project was far more complicated than its originator had foreseen. Although his design for the computer was correct, the technology of gearmaking at the time simply could not provide the precision gears needed. Costs rose and the government's financial assistance stopped. Using his own funds and borrowed monies, Babbage continued working on the project and designed an even more elaborate computer, which he called an analytical engine. This new computing engine had input and output units that used punched cards to read and record information and a computational unit that performed mathematical operations and stored information. Once again the operation of the machine depended on the use of gears—1,000 sets of them—that would assist in performing computations involving 50-digit numbers. While these grand designs were theoretically workable, in reality the machines could not be built.

Babbage spent much of his life and personal fortune trying to construct these wonderful engines that would transform science and mathematics. The task turned him from a lively and personable young man into an angry and frustrated individual who died in 1871 without achieving his goal. In his vision of the analytical engine, Babbage had foreseen the modern digital computer, a device whose existence is dependent on the electronic technology of the latter 20th century. Although Babbage himself was unable to build such a computer, his ideas and visionary zeal entitle him to be regarded as the Father of Modern Computing.

Name _____ Date _____

Charles Babbage

The following questions and investigations are intended to broaden a historical understanding of the persons and issues examined. They should provoke thinking and guide further research on the subjects under discussion. In several instances, library resources may have to be consulted.

1. Babbage worked with the British mathematicians George Peacock (1791–1858) and Augustus De Morgan (1806–1871). What were some of their mathematical accomplishments?

   _____

   _____

   _____

2. Why should Babbage have been concerned about developing an accurate logarithmic table?

   _____

   _____

   _____

3. How does the United States government support scientific activities?

   _____

   _____

   _____

4. What are some of the disadvantages of depending on a government to support scientific research?

   _____

   _____

   _____

5. The careers of two women mathematicians touched on Babbage's career. They were Ada Byron Lovelace (1815–1852) and Mary Fairfax Somerville (1780–1872). What were the mathematical accomplishments of these women?

   _____

   _____

   _____

Sir William Rowan Hamilton (1805–1865)

Ireland's Greatest Mathematician

1805–1865

William Rowan Hamilton was the third child in a family of nine children born to a Dublin attorney and his wife. When William was still very young, both his parents died and he was left in the care of an uncle. The young Hamilton soon demonstrated his talents as not only a prodigy but also a very versatile prodigy. By the age of three he was considered advanced in arithmetic; at four he knew geography; by five he read Latin, Greek, and Hebrew, and then went on to become fluent in other European languages. When he was about ten years old he began learning Oriental languages and soon added Arabic and Sanskrit to his list. At fourteen he wrote a poem of welcome in the Persian language for a visiting Persian ambassador. Writing poetry would remain a lifelong joy and hobby for him.

Hamilton became seriously interested in the study of mathematics when he was 15 years old, and two years later he entered Trinity College, Dublin, to study the subject in depth. At about this same time his great mathematical skill was first noted by the Royal Irish Academy when he called to their attention an error in Laplace's great work, *Celestial Mechanics*. The academy's president referred to Hamilton as "the first mathematician of his age," a title he was to uphold.

In 1827 when Hamilton was only 21 years old, he was appointed royal astronomer of Ireland, director of the Dunsink Observatory, and professor of astronomy at Trinity College, University of Dublin.

Learning Activities from the History of Mathematics

During the following years, he distinguished himself in many fields of pure and applied mathematics: optics, dynamics, differential equations, and the theory of equations. In his considerations of the physical world, he believed that the mathematical concepts of space and time were particularly important and felt that, while geometry was the key to understanding space, algebra would provide a science for studying time. He set to work extending the concept of algebra and soon developed an algebra for the still mysterious complex numbers. This algebra depended on viewing complex numbers of the form $a + bi$ as ordered pairs (a, b) and working with such ordered pairs. Hamilton then sought to extend this algebra to ordered triples and indeed n-tuples, but he could not work out a satisfying process of multiplication for his strange new numbers.

In 1835 he was knighted for his work in optics and became Sir William Rowan Hamilton. Still the problem of developing an algebra for n-tuples plagued him; for over ten years he thought about it. Then on October 16, 1843, while walking with his wife along the Royal Canal in Dublin, he had a flash of insight—multiplication in his algebra did not have to be commutative! His noncommutative algebra was perfectly consistent—it worked. Such a discovery had a revolutionary effect on algebraic thinking; now, many new and different algebras could be invented and used. Hamilton published his theories in 1853 in a book entitled *Treatise on Quaternions*. While quaternions themselves (his n-tuples) did not become popular, the theory they were built on led to the study and development of vector spaces, one of the most useful mathematical tools of present-day science and technology.

Hamilton's later life was unhappy. His wife became an invalid, and he became an alcoholic. When he died in 1865, his work was taken up by a host of researchers and scientists, including the American mathematician Josiah Gibbs (1839–1903). Hamilton earned the distinction of being elected the first foreign member of the newly formed National Academy of Science of the United States as well as being remembered as Ireland's greatest mathematician.

Questions and Investigations

Sir William Rowan Hamilton

The following questions and investigations are intended to broaden a historical under-standing of the persons and issues examined. They should provoke thinking and guide further research on the subjects under discussion. In several instances, library resources may have to be consulted.

1. Hamilton corrected an error in a book written by Pierre-Simon Laplace (1749–1827). Who was Laplace and what did he do?

   _____

   _____

   _____

2. Hamilton worked in many areas of mathematics and his name is associated with several mathematical concepts. Find two instances where Hamilton's name is used to identify a mathematical concept or technique.

   _____

   _____

   _____

3. Why is the study of time important in mathematics?

   _____

   _____

   _____

4. Give an example of a noncommutative operation in either mathematics or science.

   _____

   _____

   _____

5. Identify some accomplishments of Josiah Gibbs.

   _____

   _____

   _____

George Boole (1815–1864)

A Cobbler's Son

1815–1864

George Boole was born in Lincoln, England, in 1815. His father was a cobbler who also had interests in mathematics and the building of optical instruments. Young Boole attended the local elementary school but, as the family business failed, he was forced to continue his education through self-study. His father helped him with the learning of mathematics, and a local scholar assisted him in studying Latin. Through his own efforts Boole went on to acquire knowledge of German, French, and Greek. He did so well learning languages that it appeared he might become a classical scholar. By the age of 15 he became a teacher and established his own school in Lincoln.

In the year 1834 a technical institute was founded in the town of Lincoln. Boole obtained access to the institute's reading room and used its references to study higher mathematics. His talent for the subject soon became apparent. He began to contribute papers to the *Cambridge Mathematical Journal* and to the British Royal Society. In 1844 the Royal Society awarded him a medal for a paper on calculus. Five years later he applied for a position of professor of mathematics at Queen's College, Cork, Ireland, and got the position despite the fact that he did not have a university degree.

Boole was a prolific writer, producing books and papers on differential equations, finite difference methods, the theory of probability, and mathematical logic. It was in this last field that he acquired his lasting fame. In 1847 Boole published a book entitled *Investigation of the Laws of Thought* in which he established the laws of formal logic and devised a new algebra, the algebra of sets, which today is known as Boolean algebra. Bertrand Russell (1872–1970), the famous 20th-century mathematician and philosopher, would later comment, "Pure mathematics was discovered by Boole in a work which he called *The Laws of Thought*." Boolean algebra eventually found a wide range of applications in electronic circuit design. In particular, it has proven very useful in the design of modern high-speed computers that rely on a binary system of digital coding.

George Boole married Mary Everest, the niece of Sir George Everest, the explorer for whom Mount Everest was named. Throughout his stay at Queen's College, Boole was known as a conscientious teacher who prepared his lectures well. Perhaps he was too conscientious a teacher. One day in 1864, after walking two miles in a cold drenching rain, he arrived in class soaking wet but refused to cancel the lecture. As a result of this experience he developed pneumonia and died a few days later. The accomplished mathematical career of the self-taught cobbler's son had come to an untimely end.

Name _____ Date _____

George Boole

The following questions and investigations are intended to broaden a historical understanding of the persons and issues examined. They should provoke thinking and guide
further research on the subjects under discussion. In several instances, library resources may
have to be consulted.

1. George Boole possessed talents in both language and mathematics. Do you think that
   these two fields of learning are related? Explain your answer.

   _____

   _____

   _____

2. How are finite differences used? In what kind of mathematics would you find their use?

   _____

   _____

   _____

3. What were some of the accomplishments of Bertrand Russell?

   _____

   _____

   _____

4. Why do most modern electronic computers use binary mathematics?

   _____

   _____

   _____

5. Boole became a professor of mathematics even though he did not have a university
   degree. Do you think someone today could become a professor without having a
   university degree?

   _____

   _____

   _____

Sonya Kovalevskaya (1850–1891)

Russian Mathematician

1850–1891

In the middle of the 19th century, Russia was in a great state of social and economic turmoil. The serfs had been freed, education was modernized, and emphasis on industrialization increased. Into this time of change was born a woman, Sonya Krukovsky Kovalevskaya, who herself would become an agent of change. Her family were aristocrats, landholders with large estates. Her father was a retired general of artillery. As was appropriate for a girl of her social status, she received her early education at home attended by governesses and tutors.

Peter, a favorite uncle who visited frequently, enjoyed talking about mathematics; from listening to him, Sonya developed a special reverence for this "mysterious science." A curious incident in childhood also helped to introduce her to mathematics. The family's country house was renovated and its rooms wallpapered. When Sonya's room was being done, the contractor ran out of wallpaper, so some old lecture notes from General Krukovsky's student days were pasted on the wall. These were calculus notes, and Sonya spent many hours reading and trying to decipher the strange symbols and formulas on her wall. When in 1865 she finally received formal instruction in calculus, she amazed her teachers by her comprehension of the subject.

Although university reforms of 1860 permitted women to attend lectures, by 1862 these reforms had been repealed and women could no longer attain a higher education in Russia. If Russian women wished to pursue further studies they had to go abroad. To make this situation even more difficult, unmarried Russian women were not permitted to travel outside of Russia. An intellectual marriage of convenience was arranged. Sonya married another young student, Vladimir Kovalevsky, a talented writer. In 1869 they traveled to Heidelberg, Germany, where Sonya Kovalevskaya finally could study mathematics. She did well in her studies, but after a year she went on to Berlin to study under the great mathematician Karl Weierstrass (1815–1897). At the University of Berlin women were still not allowed to attend lectures, so Weierstrass had to instruct Kovalevskaya privately. At first he was skeptical of a woman mathematician, so he gave her a set of difficult problems to solve, hoping the task would drive her away from mathematics. However, she easily found solutions for the problems and demonstrated her great talent to Weierstrass, who for the next several years became her teacher.

By 1874 Kovalevskaya had adequately demonstrated an ability to do original mathematics and obtained a doctorate from the University of Göttingen. For a brief period she returned to St. Petersburg and enjoyed married life with her husband. They had a daughter and Kovalevsky became professor of paleontology at the University of Moscow. Unrest then swept Russia. Kovalevsky became involved in a failing business and committed suicide. About this time the University of Stockholm was founded. The head of its faculty of mathematics was a former student of Weierstrass and knew of Sonya Kovalevskaya's mathematical talent; he invited her to join the new faculty. She arrived in Stockholm in 1883 heralded as the Princess of Science and became the first woman university lecturer in Sweden.

In 1888 Kovalevskaya's research paper "On the Rotation of a Solid Body About a Fixed Point" won the grand prize for scientific accomplishment offered by the French Academy of Science. Besides obtaining this great honor and winning a handsome purse of 5,000 francs, Kovalevskaya became the toast of Paris, the intellectual capital of Europe. She was openly acknowledged as being a great woman mathematician. Her struggles and sacrifices had borne fruit, and her reputation would now open opportunities for other women to study mathematics.

Throughout her life, Kovalevskaya was also closely associated with literature. She enjoyed writing and likened the creative spirit of poetry to that of mathematics In 1891, at only 40 years old, Sonya Kovalevskaya died of pneumonia.

Questions and Investigations

Sonya Kovalevskaya

The following questions and investigations are intended to broaden a historical understanding of the persons and issues examined. They should provoke thinking and guide further research on the subjects under discussion. In several instances, library resources may have to be consulted.

1. Sonya's last name was Kovalevskaya and her husband's was Kovalevsky. Why were their names different?

_____

_____

_____

2. Kovalevskaya was a famous Russian mathematician. Name another well-known Russian mathematician.

_____

_____

_____

3. Kovalevskaya was called the Princess of Science. Who had the title of Prince of Mathematics?

_____

_____

_____

4. Why could Kovalevskaya attend a university in Heidelberg but not in Berlin? Weren't they both in Germany?

_____

_____

_____

5. What kind of mathematics did Karl Weierstrass undertake?

_____

_____

_____

Srinivasa Ramanujan (1887–1920)

The Man Who Loved to Compute

1887–1920

Photo courtesy of the Master and Fellows of Trinity College, Cambridge

In 1976, an American mathematician, George Andrews, was searching through some old papers stored in a library at Cambridge University. He came across a worn notebook of handwritten pages. The notebook belonged to the Indian mathematician Srinivasa Ramanujan and contained work he accomplished during the last year of his life when he was dying of tuberculosis in Madras. Its contents were extraordinary and have been described as "the equivalent of a lifetime of work of a very great mathematician." Material from this "Lost Notebook" has aided in the development of a new branch of theoretical physics, superstring theory, and one of its mathematical identities was used to devise a computer program that estimated π to an accuracy of several million digits. Who was this Indian mathematician whose work had such an impact long after his death?

Ramanujan was born into a middle-class Indian family in 1887. His father was an accountant for a cloth merchant, and his mother was recognized for her ability in astrology. He was brought up within the strict Hindu prescriptions of the Brahman caste. As a child he was described as being quiet, thoughtful, and possessing an exceptional memory. He would entertain his friends by reciting lists of Sanskrit roots as well as mathematical values for π and the square root of 2 to many decimal places. When he was 15 years old, a friend lent him a copy of Carr's *A Synopsis of Pure Mathematics*. This was mainly a book of algebraic and trigonometric formulas, but this was the first book of higher mathematics that Ramanujan had ever seen.

He set about proving the formulas and enjoyed this new activity. Thus his love for mathematics was born. Frequently he would credit his mathematical discoveries to the family goddess Namagiri, who Ramanujan said appeared to him in dreams. At age 16 he began college, aided by a government scholarship; however, within a year he lost this scholarship by failing an English test. He spent all his efforts on doing and studying mathematics. With the loss of the scholarship his formal education temporarily ended. Despite the lack of academic or scientific support, he continued his mathematical explorations, computing on a slate and recording his final results in notebooks. In 1909 he was married and accepted a position as a clerk in the Madras Port Trust. By 1911 he began publishing mathematical findings in local journals and attracted attention for his unusual results.

Several friends suggested he write to G. H. Hardy (1877-1947) at Trinity College, Cambridge, then one of the most famous mathematicians in the English-speaking world. In 1913 Ramanujan sent Hardy some of his mathematic results and sought advice on the work. Hardy was overwhelmed by what he read in this correspondence from an unknown Indian office clerk. Some of the results had been already proven by great mathematicians; others were unknown, and Hardy had to work hard to arrive at their mathematical truth. Hardy obtained financial assistance for Ramanujan to come to Cambridge to study with him. During the next five years the Indian genius studied with Hardy at Cambridge and pursued his mathematical researches; but in 1917 he became ill and was diagnosed as having tuberculosis, an incurable disease at that time.

Despite his illness, Ramanujan's mind remained sharp and his interest in mathematics keen. Once while visiting Ramanujan's sickbed, Hardy said that he had arrived in a taxi that bore the dull number 1729. The bedridden patient responded that no, the number was really interesting, as it could be represented as the sum of two cubes in two different ways: $9^3 + 10^3 = 1,729 = 12^3 + 1^3$. Much of Ramanujan's work concerned number theory. J. E. Littlewood, a colleague of Hardy, noted of the Indian mathematician that "each of the positive integers was one of his personal friends." In 1919 Ramanujan returned home to India to die. During this final year of life, he produced his last notebook.

Name _____ Date _____

Questions and Investigations

Srinivasa Ramanujan

The following questions and investigations are intended to broaden a historical understanding of the persons and issues examined. They should provoke thinking and guide
further research on the subjects under discussion. In several instances, library resources may
have to be consulted.

1. Ramanujan was very poor during his student years. Can poverty prevent someone from
   doing well in mathematics? Explain your answer.

   _____

   _____

   _____

2. Do you think number theory is an important area of mathematics? Can you find an
   example where number theory helps to solve a real-life problem?

   _____

   _____

   _____

3. Who was Pierre de Fermat (1601–1665), and what is Fermat's last theorem? Why was
   the theorem in the news in 1993?

   _____

   _____

   _____

4. Do you think that an unknown mathematical genius could live today without being
   discovered?

   _____

   _____

   _____

5. What kind of mathematics did G. H. Hardy (1877–1947) accomplish?

   _____

   _____

   _____

Nicolas Bourbaki (1939–   )

The Man Who Didn't Exist

In the mid-1930's, reviews, notes, and mathematical papers authored by a certain Nicolas Bourbaki began to appear in France. By 1939 a series of books entitled *Elements of Mathematics* began to follow. Each volume was a carefully prepared discussion on the development of mathematical concepts and stressed the structure of mathematics. It seemed that the writer of such works was attempting to prepare a modern version of all of mathematics. The author of this ambitious project was the mysterious and unknown Nicolas Bourbaki. Who was this man who had a Greek name, wrote in French, and had a vast and superior knowledge of mathematics?

In 1950, a clue to N. Bourbaki's identity was given in an article titled "The Architecture of Mathematics" published in the *American Mathematical Monthly*. A footnote to this article identified "Professor N. Bourbaki, formerly of the Royal Poldavian Academy, now residing in Nancy, France, is the author of a comprehensive treatise of modern mathematics, in course of publication under the title *Éléments de Mathématique* (Herman et Cie, Paris 1939–   ), of which ten volumes have appeared so far." Gradually, Professor Bourbaki's true identity became better known in the mathematical community.

Bourbaki was not a man but a pseudonym for a group of French mathematicians who were dedicated to the collective task of rewriting all of mathematics from a rigorous, modern, axiomatic viewpoint. According to legend (and there are many legends surrounding the Bourbaki), 50 years ago students training at the French École Normale Supérieure, an elite school for educating mathematicians, were given lectures once a year by a distinguished visitor, Nicolas Bourbaki. These lectures were really mathematical nonsense impressively delivered by an actor—a joke on the students. Later, when the group of now-renowned mathematicians agreed on their project to rewrite mathematics, they chose the whimsical name Nicolas Bourbaki as a collective pseudonym. Although the Bourbaki remains a secret group who meet once a year to plan their continued writing activities, several former members of this elite club have become known: André Weil, Jean Dieudonné, Claude Chevallier, and Henri Cartan. The composition of the group changes, as members must retire when they become 50 years old to allow younger mathematicians to take their places.

While the Bourbaki are still undertaking serious and important mathematical work, they continue to remain a source of humorous incidents in the world of mathematics. For example, several years ago the American Mathematical Society was having a meeting on the campus of the University of Illinois. A university official inspecting the facilities to be used by the visiting mathematicians found a small cobwebbed and dusty room with a plaque on the door identifying the office as belonging to N. Bourbaki. The room contained a broken chair, an old desk with an antique inkwell and quill pen, and a candle in an empty wine bottle—but no sign of Mr. Bourbaki. On another occasion the American mathematician Ralph Boas wrote an entry for the *Encyclopaedia Britannica* in which he stated that Nicolas Bourbaki did not exist. In turn the Bourbaki circulated a rumor that Boas did not exist and that the name was a collective pseudonym of a group of young American mathematicians.

In describing their work the Bourbaki have likened mathematics to a ball of twine that has many loose strings hanging from it. They believe their task is to concentrate on the tight ball of twine itself; that is, the basic fundamental core of all mathematics, and this is what their writings concern. As of 1990, 38 volumes of the Bourbaki's great work had been completed.

Questions and Investigations

Bourbaki

    The following questions and investigations are intended to broaden a historical understanding of the persons and issues examined. They should provoke thinking and guide further research on the subjects under discussion. In several instances, library resources may have to be consulted.

1. It is known that Nicolas Bourbaki was an actual historical person, although not in any manner associated with mathematics. Who was the "real" N. Bourbaki?

    _____

    _____

    _____

2. It is sometimes said that the Bourbaki's work helped to stimulate the "new math" movement of the 1960's. What was the "new math"?

    _____

    _____

    _____

3. André Weil is a famous French mathematician. What are some of his accomplishments?

    _____

    _____

    _____

4. Do you think that unifying mathematics by using one group of people's view of the subject can limit mathematical creativity?

    _____

    _____

    _____

5. What field of mathematics occupies Ralph Boas?

    _____

    _____

    _____

Reports and Research Projects

While using anecdotes and brief historical sketches certainly helps introduce students to the names and work of historical persons, students will gain a deeper understanding of the human and personal side of mathematics through more thorough research into the lives and work of individual mathematicians or groups of mathematicians. Identifying an individual name with a person who had a specific place and date of birth, a record of schooling, participation in a family life, and an attraction to mathematics helps demystify the subject. In many respects, mathematics was developed by ordinary men and women who through their persistence and special insights on the subject formulated the discipline that we know today. The development of mathematics is truly a collective, diverse, and evolutionary endeavor.

Reports on the lives and work of mathematicians can be very brief. See the following sample assignments. Such reports can be either oral or written, submitted as an individual or as a group effort, and shared with classmates. Reports can serve as a basis for extra-credit work or as enrichment units. Many excellent mathematical biographies exist for student consultation—for example, Lawrence Young's *Mathematicians and Their Times* (1981), E. T. Bell's, *Men of Mathematics* (1986), G. W. Dunnington's *Carl Friedrich Gauss: Titan of Science* (1955), and Louis Moore's *Isaac Newton: A Biography* (1962). A fuller listing of biographical works is supplied in the bibliography at the end of this book. To make reports more challenging, assign themes for students to investigate—for example, "16th-Century Algebraists," "The Circle Squares," or cooperative relations between mathematicians, such as "Teacher and Pupil" or "Father and Son." Still another approach is to assign topics of investigation involving particular mathematical problems, ones which within themselves have a long history—for example, "Euclid's Fifth Postulate" or "The Constructibility of Regular Polygons."

Following are some sample assignments that have been used successfully in classrooms.

Assignment 1
The Journey of Magellan

Fernào de Magalhàes, better known to us as Ferdinand Magellan, was a Portuguese adventurer and navigator. Employed by King Charles I of Spain, Magellan organized and carried out an expedition to establish a western sea route to the Spice Islands of the Indies. He planned his trip for several years and obtained 5 ships and a crew of about 277 men. After carefully provisioning the ships, he set out with his fleet from southern Spain on September 20, 1519. During the journey of three years Magellan did find a western route to the Spice Islands and in the process named the Pacific Ocean and discovered the Philippine Islands. In the Philippines, Magellan became involved in a tribal war in which he was killed on April 27, 1521. Although his remaining ships returned to Spain in September of 1522 without their leader, Magellan is given credit as the first explorer to circumnavigate the globe.

Magellan's crew sought fresh food and water whenever they made a landfall, but their basic store of supplies was important for the success of the expedition. Let's examine the food supply that Magellan brought with him and his crew.

His ship carried 7 cows, 3 pigs, a supply of 2,856 dried fish, 250 strings of garlic and onions, 16 small flasks of figs, and the following:

Food Item	Amount in Spanish Units	Amount in Metric Units
almonds in shells	12 cwts.	
anchovies	200 barrels	
beans and lentils	142 cwts.	
biscuits	2.136 quintals, 3 lbs.	
cheeses	112 arrobas	
currants	2 quintals	
dried pork	57 quintals, 12 lbs.	
flour	5 pipes	
honey	54 arrobas, 2 lbs.	
mustard	1 cwt.	
olive oil	47 quintals, 3 lbs.	
raisins	18 quintals	
rice	3 quintals, 22 lbs.	
vinegar	200 arrobas	
water	396 hogsheads	
wine	508 butts	

Convert the quantities of Magellan's supplies into modern-day metric units.

Assignment 2
Extra-Credit Reports on Notable Mathematicians

Mathematics is a science that has built up over thousands of years. Many men and women have contributed to its growth. You should be aware of the names and accomplishments of some of these people.

Research the lives and accomplishments of some of the mathematicians listed below. Use the historical sketch report forms. Supply all the information requested. You may choose as many or as few mathematicians to research as you wish.

Notable Mathematicians

Archimedes
Apollonius
al-Khwarizmi
al-Kashi
Aryabhata I
Charles Babbage
Jakob Bernoulli
Bhāskara
János Bolyai
George Boole
Brahmagupta
Georg Cantor
Girolamo Cardano
Nicolaus Copernicus
Augustus De Morgan
René Descartes
Diophantus
Albert Einstein
Eratosthenes
Euclid
Leonhard Euler
Pierre de Fermat
Fibonacci
Gottlob Frege
Galileo Galilei
Evariste Galois
Carl Friedrich Gauss
Sophie Germain
Kurt Gödel
W. R. Hamilton
David Hilbert

Hypatia
Omar Khayyám
Johannes Kepler
Felix Klein
Sonya Kovalevskaya
Joseph Louis Lagrange
Gottfried W. Leibniz
Liu Hui
Marin Mersenne
John Napier
Isaac Newton
Emmy Noether
Omar Khayyám
Blaise Pascal
Pythagoras
Srinivasa Ramanujan
Regiomontanus (Johannes Müller)
Bernhard Riemann
Bertrand Russell
Simon Stevin
James Sylvester
Niccolò Tartaglia
Thales
Evangelista Torricelli
Tsu Ch'ung-chih
François Viète
John von Neumann
Alfred North Whitehead
Yang Hui
Zeno of Elea

Historical Sketch Report Form

Mathematician's Name:	
Date of Birth:	Place of Birth:
Date of Death:	Place of Death:

Three events in the mathematician's life—date also if known
1.
2.
3.

Three accomplishments in mathematics
1.
2.
3.

Three facts of interest about your mathematician
1.
2.
3.

Sources
1.
2.
3.

Name _____ Date _____

Sample

Mathematician's Name: **Carl Friedrich Gauss**	
Date of Birth: **April 30, 1777**	Place of Birth: **Brunswick, Germany**
Date of Death: **February 23, 1855**	Place of Death: **Göttingen**

Three events in the mathematician's life—date also if known

1. **From 1795–98 he went to secondary school and studied further at the University of Göttingen, supported by the duke of Brunswick.**

2. **In 1799 he obtained his doctorate in absentia from the University of Heimstedt. His thesis showed the first proof of fundamental algebra, which states that every algebraic equation has a root of $a + bi$ (i being the square root of −1).**

3. **In 1807 he became professor of astronomy and director of the new observatory at the University of Göttingen, where he remained for the rest of his life.**

Three accomplishments in mathematics

1. **He discovered the method of least squares.**

2. **He discovered a non-Euclidean geometry.**

3. **He contributed to the theory of numbers.**

Three facts of interest about your mathematician

1. **Gauss was deeply religious, aristocratic in bearing, and conservative.**

2. **Gauss has been acknowledged to be one of the three leading mathematicians of all times; the other two being Archimedes and Newton.**

3. **Gauss was an exceptionally precocious child. At age three he detected an error in his father's bookkeeping. At ten he amazed his teachers and fellow students by summing the integers from 1 to 100 in just a few minutes.**

Sources

1. *Encyclopedia Americana*

2. *Encyclopaedia Britannica*

3. *The Papers of Carl Gauss*

Name _____   Date _____

Women in Mathematics

Any consideration of the history of mathematics should stress the global and universal nature of mathematical investigations and advances. Far too often the history of mathematics as presented in texts and popular materials is Euro-centered and male-dominated. Quite simply, this is bias. Non-European mathematical contributions—that is, those of Hindu, Chinese, and Islamic cultures—are minimized in favor of traditions founded on the contributions of early western Mediterranean societies, principally the Greek. This historical phenomenon of bias has frequently been caused by language barriers and limited scholarship. Teachers must be aware of this situation and attempt, when possible, to rectify the situation. Some good survey works on the history of non-Western mathematics are now appearing.

Due mainly to Western cultural barriers, women and their contributions have not been amply represented in the history of mathematics. This situation is also changing, but we can accelerate it by actively calling attention to the historical contributions of women. Here is a list of some notable women from the history of mathematics:

Name	Dates	Field of Activity
Hypatia	ca. 370–415	Astronomy and mechanics
Marquise du Châtelet	1706–1749	Analysis
Maria Agnesi	1718–1799	Analysis
Sophie Germain	1776–1831	Number theory
Mary Fairfax Somerville	1780–1872	Celestial mechanics
Ada Lovelace	1815–1852	Computing
Sonya Kovalevskaya	1850–1891	Analysis
Charlotte Scott	1858–1931	Algebraic geometry
Grace Chisholm Young	1868–1944	Foundations
Emmy Noether	1882–1935	Noncommutative algebras
Grace Hopper	1906–1992	Computer science

For specific references on non-Western mathematics and the lives and work of women mathematicians, see the bibliography at the end of this book.

Title page illustration from a 16th-century book.
What mathematical applications does it depict?

CHAPTER 3

History in a Few Words

Years ago when I was teaching a 3rd-grade class, one of my students, a little girl, asked me, "Why, when we write down a weight, do we use the abbreviation *lb.* for pounds? *Pounds* is spelled with a *p*. Why don't we use *p.* for pounds?" A thoughtful question. Even the English currency *pounds* is abbreviated by an *L*, not a *P*. Why is this? I did not have an immediate answer for this question and it prompted me to do some research on the subject. I found out that this notation has Roman origins. The Romans actually used the letter *p* from their word *pendo*, "to weigh out," to abbreviate units of weight. However, their word for "pound" was *libra*, a word adopted into the later Italian. Medieval merchants abbreviated their libra unit of weight by the letters *lb*, a practice that has continued until the present day. As for the British pound currency, the early European unit of currency was a pound of silver—again, the word *libra* and the use of *L* as an abbreviation, which the British have retained.

More recently a colleague who knew of my interest in the history of mathematics asked, "Why are second-degree equations called 'quadratic equations'? It seems that the prefix *quad* designates a 'fourness' and is out of context in speaking about a second-degree equation." Of course, his reasoning was correct. Once again I had no immediate answer, but after thinking about the question for a day and checking some books, I could satisfy his inquiry.

Both of these instances illustrate how even the terms and phrases, the words of mathematics, can convey a history. They have stories to tell—stories that are sometimes fascinating, frequently amusing, and, more importantly, reflect the development and growth of mathematics.

Word Origins

By supplying your students with the etymological origins of mathematical terms, you give the terms added meaning and, in a simple manner, impart a historical sense to what you are teaching. These brief word-origin encounters help students appreciate the universal and evolutionary nature of mathematics. The following potpourri of etymological anecdotes and memorabilia is offered as a stimulus of ideas and a resource if you wish to explore mathematical words with your students.

The word *mathematics* comes from the ancient Greek word *mathematikos*, which means "disposed to learning." (Can we say our students are mathematikos?)

Arithmetic is derived from the Greek *arithmos*, "number." In Latin this became *arithmetica*, and through Old French it evolved into its present English-language form.

Number originated in the Latin *numerus*, which in Old French became *nombre* and in German *nummer*, finally emerging in English as *number*.

Numeral evolved from the Latin *numeralis*, "concerning numbers."

English-language number names emerged through German and Anglo-Saxon. The decimal nature of our number system is illustrated by such words as *eleven* from the Old German composite of *ein-lif*, "one" and "ten"; *twelve* from *zwo-lif*, "two" and "ten." *Zero*, however, has a more interesting etymological history that can be traced back to the Hindu word *sunya*, "the void," which in Arabic became *sifr*, "empty." This passed into Italian as *zefirum*, *zefiro*, and *zefro*, which in the Ventian dialect became *zero*. Via another linguistic route, *sifr* was translated into German as *cifra* and in English became *cipher*. Thus the original word for zero has given us two mathematical terms.

At the other extreme of the number scale, *million* comes from the Italian *millione*, "a greater thousand," which is built on the Latin *mille*, "a thousand." *Mille* has supplied us with many mathematical terms, including *mile*, (the Roman mile was a thousand paces, *mille passus*), *millimeter*, *millennium*.

Our terms for designating integers as either *odd* or *even* are due to the Old Norse word *oddi* and the Anglo-Saxon *efen*.

We sometimes refer to numerals as *digits*, which goes back to the Latin word for "fingers," *digiti*, and reflects on the early use of fingers as computing aids.

Someone may be described as being "good at *figures*," a phrase that pertains to the figurative numbers of the ancient Greeks.

Occasionally, when counting objects, we may make *tallies*. The word *tally* has a long and interesting mathematical history reaching back to the Roman word *talley*, whose Latin ancestor was *talea*, "to cut a twig." In the Middle Ages, this word evolved into the French *talare* and *taille*, from which the word *tailor* is derived, and finally into English as *tally*. For thousands of years, mathematical recordings have been made by carving notches on a stick or bone. In Europe, loan contracts were actually made by cutting such notches into a stick, or *stock*. The stock was broken, and the "broker" ("stockbroker") kept the long end of the stick, while the debtor got "the short end of the stick." Apparently the ancient Chinese also used tally sticks in their business dealings. The Chinese written character for the word **contract** is composed of three smaller characters: one meaning "tally stick"; another, "knife"; and the third, "large." Thus for the Chinese, a large tally stick was a contract.

Of course, we **calculate** with numbers. This word comes from the Latin *calculi*, "little stones," and reflects the use of tally pebbles on a counting board. **Calculus** has the same ancestor. The word **compute** is from the Latin *computare*, to reckon. It passed into French as *comptoures* and in German became *Kontor*, from which English derived **counter**, which designated a computing board or abacus over which medieval business was transacted. Today, in a store, we do business "over the counter."

Medieval counters were a form of **abacus**, a Latin word derived from the Greek *abax*, "small table," which physically describes the early abaci. The head of the British Royal Treasury is called the **exchequer**. This title describes the computing table used in early England, a *chequer*, from which comes our concept of *checkerboard*. However, the act of using this computing board to affirm the accuracy of accounts was *to check*. Later the word **check** became applied to bank drafts.

Many mathematical terms trace their origins to words that were associated with the counting board and its operation. **Reckon** comes from the German *Recken*, "to rake in" or "put in order," that is, to arrange counters on a counting board. In the operation of **addition**, we "put together, " as described by its Latin predecessor, *addere*. In early texts, the operational word for addition was *and*, in Latin *et*. It is believed that this two-letter word evolved into the symbol +. The word **subtraction** comes from the Latin *subtrahere*, "to draw away," again describing the physical movement of counters. Its symbol of – is probably derived from a mark used on barrels in the Middle Ages to indicate a deficiency in their contents.

When we compute with pencil and paper or even modern electronic computers, we usually use an **algorithm**, a term arrived at by the European transliteration of the name of the 9th-century Arabic scholar al-Khwarizmi.

Fraction comes from the Latin *frangere*, "to break." Quite literally a fraction is a broken number. Its parts retain their Latin names: *numerator*, "the number," and *denominator*, "the namer." The custom of using a bar to separate the parts of a fraction was inherited from the Arabs and first introduced into Europe by Leonardo of Pisa in the 13th century. A thousand years earlier, the ancient Chinese also expressed common fractions as a vertical array of two numbers; however, they placed the denominator, which they called "the mother," on top, and the numerator, "the son," on the bottom. The Chinese also developed the convention of using the colors red and black to designate positive and negative numbers,

Learning Activities from the History of Mathematics

but once again, their convention was opposite to ours. They used red for positive numbers and black for negatives ones.

Irrational numbers have always held a special place in arithmetic. Medieval scholars termed irrational numbers *numerus sudus*, or "inaudible numbers"; this term resulted from the use of an Arabic translation of the ancient Greek word *alogos*, irrational.

Our number system is *decimal* in nature. The word *decimal* comes from the original Latin *decimus*, "ten." An interesting cousin of this word is *decimate*, which was the Roman practice when disciplining a legion of soldiers to punish every tenth man (*decimatio*) for group infraction of rules. In case of a mutiny, this punishment was death. This situation gave rise to a famous mathematical problem, the Josephus problem, where in a given situation you would have to arrange yourself so as not to be the tenth person in an ordering even after several rounds of punishment were administered.

During the Middle Ages, the Roman Catholic Church had severe restrictions regarding money-lending and possible instances of usury. According to Church policy, a borrower paid nothing on a loan provided it was repaid within a specified time period. If, however, the principal was not repaid within the allotted time, the borrower had to compensate the lender by a sum that represented the difference between the loan and the amount repaid, or "that which is between," which in the official Latin of the period was *id quod interest*. The last word of this phrase, *interest*, remains today to describe the transaction.

Many terms of modern-day business arithmetic owe their origins to Italian mercantile activity of the Middle Ages: *discount*, *disconto*; *debit*, *debito*; *credit*, *credito*; *value*, *valuta*; *gross*, *grosso*; *cash*, from *cassa*, "money chest." Counting tables were called *banca*, thus, *banks*. If a moneylender was found to be dishonest, his table was publicly smashed, *banca-rupta*. Today, we would say he went *bankrupt*. Italian merchant agents abroad were called *factors* and their warehouses, *factories*. The word *factor* comes from the Latin *facere*, "to do or operate," and has remained with us as a term in mathematics. Both the word *percent* and its symbol were also a result of Italian merchant activity. *Per cento*, "by the hundred," was abbreviated as *pc°* and finally symbolized as %.

Algebra evolved from the Arabic *al-jabr*, *al* meaning "the," and *jabr* meaning "restoring," describing the process of "restoring" a mathematical statement from its pieces. The word found its way into Europe in the 9th-century through the works of al-Khwarizmi. Italian mathematicians of a later period called the unknown quantities they worked with *cosa*, "things," and their discipline became the *Cossic art*. Historically the name *algebra* survived. Much of early algebraic theory came from the Arabs. They spoke of the "root of a number"; this term translated into Latin as *radices* and has become our *radical*. The modern words *tariff* and *degree* also have Arabic origins.

The expressions to *square* and to *cube* a number follow from the intuitive Greek concept of figurate numbers, that is, numbers that could be enumerated by counters arranged in a physical configuration. Squares represent square numbers: 1, 4, 9, ... A three-dimensional analogy, a cube, gives cubic numbers: 1, 8, 27, ... *Quadrare* is the Latin word

Learning Activities from the History of Mathematics

meaning "to make square," so an equation obtained by squaring terms is called a ***quadratic*** equation. The words ***equation*** and ***equals*** are from the Latin *aequalis*, "equal."

Geometry owes its origin to the Greek words for "earth," *geo*, and "measurement," *met'ron*, and reflects the concrete aspects of early geometric activity.

Trigonometry is from the Greek *trigonon*, "triangle," and *met'ron*, "measure." Unlike the word *geometry*, the term *trigonometry* was probably never used by the Greeks themselves. Constructed by later European scholars, it was a word that first appeared in mathematical literature in 1590.

The term for ***sine***, as in sine of an angle, originated with the Hindus, who referred to it as *jya*, "chord." Transliterated into Arabic this became *jaib*, "bosom," and no doubt caused some confusion concerning the preoccupation of mathematicians. The word found its way into Latin in about 1150 as *sinus*, "fold," and later into English as the word *sine*. Regiomontanus (ca. 1463) used the expression *sinus rectus complementi* to designate ***cosine***; by 1620, Edmund Gunter (1581–1626) had abbreviated this to *co. sinus*, and finally in 1658, Isaac Newton used the term *cosine*.

Statistics is from the Latin word *stato*, "state," via the descendant form, *statista*, "politician," or "one who serves the state." Statistics were therefore originally facts that pertained to the state.

A rich category of mathematical lore can be found in an examination of the terms used to designate currency, weights, and measures. For example, ***penny*** traces its origin to the Latin *pendo*, "to weigh," and indicates that units of early currency were actually designated weights, usually of a valued metal. Our word ***dime*** comes from the French *dîme*, "tenth." ***Dollar*** evolved from the Old German *Thaler,* which was a large coin used in the Middle Ages. In early America, many different currencies were used, including in many cases the Mexican dollar, or *peso*. In financial transactions, a symbol was used to indicate pesos: $p^s \rightarrow \$\,p \rightarrow \$$. Thus our dollar sign came from the Mexican peso.

Both ***ounce*** and ***inch*** can be traced to the same Latin word, *unciae*, the twelfth part of a Roman pound and a basic fraction in Roman metrology. The abbreviation of *ounce* as "***oz.***" is fairly recent and comes from the early California gold-mining days. At that time, a Spanish coin called *onza de oro*, "ounce of gold," was widely used. The *oz* was derived from the Spanish word for "ounce," *onza*.

Precious metals are weighed in ***carats***, a corruption of the word *karob*, the name of a seed from an Abyssinian tree. Many early weights and measures were standardized as a certain number of specific seeds, such as wheat, rice, and barley.

In the Middle Ages a wine vessel of a specific size called a *gello* was used as a standard, from whence we get our ***gallon***.

Over the years rather extensive systems for capacity measure have been derived. Many such systems, although very practical and mathematically well conceived, have not survived. An interesting history of such units and an excellent source of teaching ideas is Arthur Klein's *The World of Measurement* (1974). As one example of measurement history and intrigue, consider the popular Mother Goose rhyme:

Jack and Jill went up the hill
To fetch a pail of water
Jack fell down and broke his crown
And Jill came tumbling after.

In 17th-century England, *jack*, *jill*, and *pail* were units of liquid measure and taxable by the Crown. Tax-hungry Charles I inflated his tax ("went up the hill") on the jack and jill. This unpopular act helped to insure his downfall ("broke his crown"). This simple rhyme was a political protest disguised as a children's ditty.

An example of how one teacher developed an assignment that combined world history with the history of measurement is illustrated in the sample Assignment 1.

Some word origins or phrase meanings are less profound mathematically but help reveal the human side of mathematics. For example, the phrase **square deal** implies a fair transaction and reflects the number mysticism of the ancient Pythagoreans, who associated a meaning and mystical power with each number. To the Pythagoreans the number 4, the first square number, represented justice. Thus squareness is associated with justice. Another similar example is the explanation of why 7 is considered to be a lucky number in our culture. In early astrology, the seven planets were regarded as messengers of the gods and bearers of good fortune. Thus, luck was associated with the number 7. It is noteworthy in this connection that the seven days of the week were named after pagan gods.

Numbers contribute to word origins in some unlikely instances. In 17th-century England a drink composed of five ingredients became very popular. It was called **punch** after the Sanskrit Hindi number word *panca*, "five." *Siesta* is Spanish for "the sixth hour." In a twelve-hour day the sixth hour would be noontime. Thus, **siesta** designates a noontime nap.

It is easy to disperse word etymologies or little word stories throughout your mathematics teaching. Once students realize the fact that even a single word can be a source of much information, they can undertake their own historical treasure hunts seeking the deeper meaning for assigned mystery words. For example:

divine proportion	gematria
golden rule	harmonic mean
sieve of Eratosthenes	friendly number
astrolabe	salinon
ENAIC	infinity
Bourbaki	arbelos
regula falsi	quaternions

Historical Quotations

Quotations can also modify and historically heighten a presentation. Consider, for example, the effects of the following words from Jacques Barzun, a respected commentator on the 20th-century American educational scene:

I have more than an impression—it amounts to a certainty—that algebra is made repellent by the unwillingness or inability of teachers to explain why. There is no sense of history behind the teaching, so the feeling is given that the whole system dropped down ready-made from the skies, to be used only by born jugglers.

The quote catches the reader's eye and the listener's ear. Association with its author gives it a sense of authority. In written form, we reread it to understand better its essence and the wisdom it conveys. The quote becomes a focal point for an idea. In the classroom, quotations relevant to and from the history of mathematics have the same effect on students. Their contents can become a stimulus for discussion: Who is the speaker? What does he mean? Why is she saying it? What episode in the history of mathematics does the quotation reflect on? These and many other questions can shape the use of quotations into true learning encounters. The following pages provide a sample listing of appropriate quotations for your possible use.

The Nature of Mathematics

"Mathematics is the queen of the sciences."

—Carl Friedrich Gauss (1777–1855)

"There is no branch of mathematics, however abstract, which may not someday be applied to phenomena of the real world."

—Nikolai Lobachevsky (1792–1856)

"The deep study of nature is the most fruitful source of mathematical discovery."

—Joseph Fourier (1768–1830)

"When we cannot use the compass of mathematics or the torch of experience . . . it is certain that we cannot take a single step forward."

—Voltaire (1694–1778)

"If there is anything that can bind the heavenly mind of man to this dreary exile of our earthy home and can reconcile us with our fate so that one can enjoy living—then it is verily the enjoyment of . . . the mathematical sciences and astronomy."

—Johannes Kepler (1571–1630)

"If we wish to foresee the future of mathematics, our proper course is to study the history and present condition of the science."

—Jules Henri Poincaré (1854–1912)

"All science, logic and mathematics included, is a function of the epoch—all science, in its ideals as well as in its achievements."

—E. H. Moore (1862–1932)

"Mathematics is the gate and key of the sciences."

—Roger Bacon (ca. 1214–1294)

"All the pictures which science now draws of nature and which alone seem capable of according with observational fact are mathematical pictures."

—Sir James Hopwood Jeans (1877–1946)

"The advancement and perfection of mathematics are intimately connected with the prosperity of the State."

—Napoleon I (1769–1821)

". . . the universe stands continually open to our gaze, but it cannot be understood unless one first learns to comprehend the language and interpret the characters in which it is written. It is written in the language of mathematics, and its characters are triangles, circles, and other geometric figures."

—Galileo (1564–1642)

"The science of pure mathematics may claim to be the most original creation of the human spirit."

—Alfred North Whitehead (1861–1947)

"It is an error to believe that rigor in proof is an enemy of simplicity. . . . The very effort of rigor forces us to find our simpler methods of proof."

—David Hilbert (1862–1943)

"The profound study of nature is the most fertile source of mathematical discoveries."

—Joseph Fourier (1768–1830)

"Logic is invincible because in order to combat logic it is necessary to use logic."

—Pierre Boutroux (1880–1922)

"Mathematics is a yoga and yoga becomes mathematics; there is no end to its depths."

—Baba Hari Dass (1923–   )

"The essence of mathematics is its freedom."

—Georg Cantor (1845–1918)

"As far as the propositions of mathematics refer to reality, they are not certain; and as far as they are certain, they do not refer to reality."

—Albert Einstein (1879–1955)

"Man is the measure of all things."

—Anonymous

"If we can approach the Divine only through symbols, then it is most suitable that we use mathematical symbols, for these have an indestructible certainty."

—Nicholas of Cusa (1401–1464)

"The moving power of mathematical invention is not reasoning but imagination."

—Augustus De Morgan (1806–1871)

"The real end of science is the honor of the human mind."

—Carl Gustav Jacob Jacobi (1804–1851)

"May not music be described as the mathematics of sense, mathematics as the music of reason?"

—J. J. Sylvester (1814–1897)

"The investigation of mathematical truths accustoms the mind to method and correctness in reasoning, and is an employment peculiarly worthy of rational beings."

—George Washington (1732–1799)

Mathematics and Mathematicians

"Do not worry about your difficulties in mathematics. I can assure you that mine are still greater."

—Albert Einstein (1879–1955)

"Imagination is more important than knowledge."

—Albert Einstein (1879–1955)

"From the intrinsic evidence of His creation, the Great Architect of the universe now begins to appear as a pure mathematician."

—Sir James Hopwood Jeans (1877–1946)

"Mathematicians are like lovers . . . . Grant a mathematician the least principle, and he will draw from it a consequence which you must also grant him, and from this consequence another."

—Fontenelle (1657–1757)

"The applied mathematician can find the solution to any difficulty, whilst the pure mathematician can find the difficulty to any solution."

—Anonymous

"I have made this letter longer than usually because I lacked the time to make it short."

—Blaise Pascal (1623–1662)

"To think the thinkable—that is the mathematician's aim."

—C. J. Keyser (1862–1947)

"In most sciences one generation tears down what another has built, and what one has established another undoes. In mathematics alone each generation adds a new story to the old structure."

—Hermann Hankel (1839–1873)

"It appears to me that if one wants to make progress in mathematics, one should study the masters and not the pupils."

—N. H. Abel (1802–1829)

"It is not possible to present its proof on the margin of this page."

—Pierre de Fermat (1601–1665)

"If I have seen further it is by standing on the shoulders of giants."

—Issac Newton (1642–1727)

"One cannot escape the feeling that these mathematical formulae have an independent existence and an intelligence of their own, that they are wiser than we are, wiser even than their discoverers . . . ."

—Heinrich Hertz (1857–1894)

"Mathematicians do not deal in objects, but in relations between objects . . . ."

—Raymond Poincaré (1860–1934)

"Mathematical entities exist independently of the activities of mathematicians in much the same way the stars would be there even if there were no astronomers to look at them."

—Kurt Gödel (1906–1978)

"The true mathematician is always a good deal of an artist, an architect, yes, a poet."

—Alfred Pringsheim (1850–1941)

"Mathematics is the science which draws necessary conclusions."

—Benjamin Peirce (1809–1880)

"The most distinct and beautiful statements of any truth must take at last the mathematical form."

—Henry David Thoreau (1817–1862)

". . . it is impossible to be a mathematician without being a poet in soul."

—Sonya Kovalevskaya (1850–1891)

"Mathematics—the unshaken Foundation of Sciences and the plentiful Fountain of Advantage to human affairs."

—Isaac Barrow (1630–1677)

"There is more imagination in the head of Archimedes than that of Homer."

—Voltaire (1694–1778)

Numbers and Arithmetic

"Music is the pleasure the human soul experiences from counting without being aware it is counting."

—Gottfried Wilhelm Leibniz (1646–1716)

"God made integers; all else is the work of man."

—Leopold Kronecker (1823–1891)

"What's one and one and one and one and one and one and one and one and one and one?"
"I don't know," said Alice. "I lost count."
"She can't do addition," said the Red Queen.

—Lewis Carroll (1832–1898)

"There still remain three studies suitable for free man. Arithmetic is one of them."

—Plato (427–347 B.C.)

"Where there is number there is beauty."

—Proclus (410–485)

"The solution of the difficulties which formerly surrounded the mathematical infinite is probably the greatest achievement of which our age has to boast."

—Bertrand Russell (1872–1970)

"When you can measure what you are talking about and express it in numbers, you know something about it."

—Lord Kelvin (1824–1907)

"People who don't count won't count."

—Anatole France (1844–1924)

"All things which can be known have number; for it is not possible that without number anything can be either conceived or known."

—Philolaus (ca. 425 B.C.)

"If arithmetic, numeration, and weighing be taken away from any art, that which remains will be little indeed."

—Plato (427–347 B.C.)

"Allusion to the general ignorance of arithmetic has . . . always been well received."

—Augustus De Morgan (1806–1871)

Geometry

"There is no royal road to geometry."

—Euclid (ca. 300 B.C.)

"It is the glory of geometry that from so few principles, fetched from without, it is able to accomplish so much."

—Isaac Newton (1642–1727)

"Geometry will draw the soul toward truth and create the spirit of philosophy."

—Plato (427–347 B.C.)

"Mighty is geometry; joined with art, resistless."

—Euripides (480–406 B.C.)

"Let no one ignorant of geometry enter this door."

—Motto on entrance to Plato's Academy

"Out of nothing I have created a strange new universe."

—János Bolyai (1802–1860)

Probability and Statistics

"A reasonable probability is the only certainty."

—E. W. Howe (1853–1937)

"...Time and chance happeneth to them all."

—Ecclesiastes

"Statistics is the logic of measurement, and all sciences require measurement."

—S. M. Stigler (1941–   )

"Statistical thinking will one day be as necessary for efficient citizenship as the ability to read and write."

—H. G. Wells (1866–1946)

"It is by the aid of statistics that law in the social sphere can be ascertained and codified."

—Florence Nightingale (1820–1910)

Algebra

"Algebra is the analytic method par excellence: It has been contrived to facilitate the operations of the understanding, to make reasoning more concise, and to contract into a few lines what would have needed many pages of discussion."

—Antoine-Laurent Lavoisier (1743–1794)

"As long as algebra and geometry proceeded along separate paths, their advance was slow and their applications limited. But when these sciences joined company, they drew from each other fresh vitality and thenceforth marched on at a rapid pace."

—Joseph-Louis Lagrange (1736–1813)

"Algebra is the intellectual instrument for rendering clear the quantitative aspects of the world."

—Alfred North Whitehead (1861–1947)

"Algebra is generous; she often gives more than is asked of her."

—Jean Le Rond d'Alembert (1717–1783)

as their woozkes doe extende) to diſtincte it onely into twoo partes. Whereof the firſte is, *when one nomber is equalle vnto one other.* And the ſeconde is, *when one nom= ber is compared as equalle vnto. 2. other nombers.*

Alwaies willyng you to remēber, that you reduce your nombers, to their leaſte denominations, and ſmalleſte fozmes, befoze you procede any farther.

And again, if your *equation* be ſoche, that the grea= teſte denomination *Coſſike,* be ioined to any parte of a compounde nomber, you ſhall tourne it ſo, that the nomber of the greateſte ſigne alone, maie ſtande as equalle to the reſte.

And this is all that neadeth to be taughte, concer= nyng this woozke.

Howbeit, foz eaſie alteratiō of *equations.* J will pzo= pounde a fewe exãples, bicauſe the extraction of their rootes, maie the moze aptly bee wzoughte. And to a= uoide the tediouſe repetition of theſe woozdes: is e= qualle to: J will ſette as J doe often in woozke vſe, a paire of paralleles, oz Gemowe lines of one lengthe, thus:===== , bicauſe noe. 2. thynges, can be moare equalle. And now marke theſe nombers.

1. $14.\math.{z\!e}.\ -\!\!\!\!|\!\!\!\!-\ .15.\mathit{q} \;=\!=\!=\!=\!=\; 71.\mathit{q}.$

2. $20.\mathit{z\!e}.\ -\!\!\!\!-\!\!\!\!-\ .18.\mathit{q} \;=\!=\!=\; .102.\mathit{q}.$

3. $26.\mathit{z}\ -\!\!\!\!|\!\!\!\!-\ 10\mathit{z\!e} \;=\!=\!=\; 9.\mathit{z}\ -\!\!\!\!-\!\!\!\!-\ 10\mathit{z\!e}\ -\!\!\!\!|\!\!\!\!-\ 213.\mathit{q}.$

4. $19.\mathit{z\!e}\ -\!\!\!\!|\!\!\!\!-\ 192.\mathit{q} \;=\!=\!=\; 10\mathit{z}\ -\!\!\!\!|\!\!\!\!-\ 108\mathit{q}\ -\!\!\!\!-\!\!\!\!-\ 19\mathit{z\!e}$

5. $18.\mathit{z\!e}\ -\!\!\!\!|\!\!\!\!-\ 24.\mathit{q}. \;=\!=\!=\; 8.\mathit{z}.\ -\!\!\!\!|\!\!\!\!-\ 2.\mathit{z\!e}.$

6. $34\mathit{z}\ -\!\!\!\!-\!\!\!\!-\ 12\mathit{z\!e} \;=\!=\!=\; 40\mathit{z\!e}\ -\!\!\!\!|\!\!\!\!-\ 480\mathit{q}\ -\!\!\!\!-\!\!\!\!-\ 9.\mathit{z}.$

First use of equals sign in arithmetic.
Who "invented" this symbol?

CHAPTER 4

Problems, Problems, Problems

Teachers are always looking for good sources of mathematical problems and exercises for classroom use, problems and exercises that will both motivate and reinforce the concepts being taught. Why not seek them out in the history of mathematics? Over 2,000 years of accumulated mathematical experiences have produced a wealth of problems and exercises whose solution-seeking can both enrich classroom lessons and be a source of extended learning in itself. Historical problems demonstrate the type of mathematics that concerned our ancestors. Their contents often illustrate the connections between mathematics and societal needs—grain storage, taxation, forming business ventures—and supply an understandable relevance, at least in the historical sense, to mathematical concepts and operations.

The original solution methods, while perhaps archaic, serve as intuitive links to the development of more modern and efficient solution schemes. For example, the interpretation and solution of a Babylonian problem from 1000 B.C. might require the solver graphically to "complete the square," that is, construct a square whose sides could be considered of length $x + b$, so that the square would possess an area given by $(x+b)^2 = x^2 + 2xb + b^2$. Then if a numerical value is given for the area, a value for x can be determined. Today, a student may use the algebraic process of completing the square and not realize just what "completing the square" means. (Do all teachers realize what completing the square means?)

Historical problems can also tell us much about the origins of mathematics, its applications, and its importance. Often these facts emerge as exciting student discoveries: "The ancient Chinese solved quadratic equations!" "The Pythagorean theorem was known and used long before Pythagoras was born." They also provide opportunities for further mathematical exploration and discovery: "The Babylonians could find a value for $\sqrt{2}$ accurately to six decimal places without a calculator. How did they do it?"

Problems from the history of mathematics fall into two categories: those that are contrived, that is, problems or exercises constructed around a historical mathematical concept—the question is modern, the concept is old; and actual problems that were posed and solved by our mathematical ancestors—the question is old and the concept is old. Each type of problem possesses certain inherent learning benefits.

Construed problems can be teacher-constructed for specific teaching purposes or emphasis. Consider some particular teaching situations and how you might devise historically based problems to satisfy them. For example, a geometry teacher wants to provide practice in spatial reasoning. She discusses the five Platonic solids with her class, noting their special importance to the ancient Greeks. Then, as a homework assignment, she asks the class to prove that only five such solids exist. Again building on a knowledge of Platonic solids, a more rigorous problem-solving challenge can be offered to a more advanced class, such as an Algebra II class. Each of the Platonic solids are circumscribable, that is, a sphere can be constructed around each solid so that its vertices coincide with the surface of the sphere. Johannes Kepler used this fact in deriving cosmological models of the universe. If for each of these polyhedra, the length of an edge is known, say x, can the class find the length of the radii for the circumscribing spheres?

Consider another instance. An Algebra I teacher stressing pattern recognition and inductive reasoning methods might introduce a class to the Fibonacci sequence:

$$1, 1, 2, 3, 5, 8, 13, 21, \ldots$$

Then the teacher could discuss its historical background and work with the students to see how the sequence is formed. After this introduction, the teacher designates the nth Fibonacci number by F_n and asks the students to verify or perhaps even prove a number of relationships such as:

$$F_n = F_{n-1} + F_{n-2}$$
$$F_n^2 = F_{n-1} F_{n+1} + -1^{n-1} \quad n \geq 2$$
$$F_1^2 + F_2^2 + F_3^2 + \ldots + F_n^2 = F_n F_{n+1}$$

While Fibonacci probably never worried about such relationships, they are interesting exercises for contemporary students. You can easily generate problems such as these if you have some knowledge of the history of mathematics, or you can find them in existing collections of problems. Two excellent sources of problems are Eves, *An Introduction to the History of Mathematics* (1983) and Burton, *The History of Mathematics: An Introduction* (1991).

Actual historical problems, while they may not always be as mathematically fruitful as their derived counterparts, convey many of the desirable historical features already discussed, due to their authenticity. Such problems transport their readers back into another time and place and, most often, into a different cultural setting. Students might find themselves computing a dowry price or determining the pasturage for farm animals, novelties that are often motivating in themselves. You can modify the intensity of the problems at your discretion. For example, you might convert Babylonian problems where numerical values are expressed in base 60 to base 10 notation before assigning them. Similarly, you can convert archaic units of measure to a convenient modern form. However, occasionally working with historical units of measurement also provides learning benefits—for example, the ancient Chinese used a decimal system with 10 inches to a foot for their linear measurement requirements. An abundance of these problems also exist in various sources. Some specific sources of problems are given in the bibliography at the end of this book. A sample selection of problems is also offered here for your use. Most of the following are appropriate for use with algebra or geometry classes.

A Selection of Historical Problems

Egypt

Rhind Papyrus (1650 B.C.): *A collection of 85 problems and their solutions compiled by the scribe Ahmes. It is believed that he used material from 1800 B.C. in the problem collection. The scroll that contained the problems was purchased in Egypt in 1858 by a Scotsman, A. Henry Rhind, who later gave it to the British Museum.*

1. Divide 100 loaves among 10 men including a boatman, a foreman, and a doorkeeper, who receive double portions. What is the share of each?

   Answer: regular share, $7\frac{9}{13}$ loaves; special share, $15\frac{5}{13}$ loaves

2. How many cattle are in a herd when $\frac{2}{3}$ of $\frac{1}{3}$ of them make 70, the number due as tribute to the owner?

   Answer: 315

3. Suppose a scribe says to you that 4 overseers have drawn 100 great quadruple *hekat* of grain, and their gangs consist of 12, 8, 6, and 4 men. How much does each overseer receive?

   Answer: 40, $26\frac{2}{3}$, 20, $13\frac{1}{3}$

4. Compare the area of a circle with its circumscribed square.

   Answer: circle ÷ square = $\frac{\pi}{4}$

5. A cylindrical granary has a diameter of 9 cubits and a height of 10 cubits. What is the amount of grain that goes in it?

   Answer: 636.173 cubits^3

6. Find $\frac{1}{3}$ of $1 + \frac{1}{3} + \frac{1}{4}$.

   Answer: $\frac{19}{36}$

7. A quantity and its $\frac{1}{5}$ added together become 21. What is the quantity?

   Answer: $17\frac{1}{2}$

8. A quantity, its $\frac{1}{3}$, and its $\frac{1}{4}$ added together become 2. What is the quantity?

   Answer: $1\frac{5}{19}$

Cairo Papyrus (250 B.C.): *A collection of 40 problems, 9 of which concern right triangles. The scroll was found in 1938 and finally translated in 1962.*

9. An erect pole of 10 cubits has its base moved 6 cubits. Determine the new height and the distance the top of the pole is lowered.

    Answer: 8 cubits; 2 cubits

10. It is said to you, "Have sailcloth made for the ships," and it is further said, "Allow 1,000 cloth cubits [square cubits] for one sail and have the ratio of the height of the sail to its width be 1 to $1\frac{1}{2}$." What is the height of the sail?

    Answer: 25.82 cubits

11. As for a piece of land that amounts to 100 square cubits that is square, if it is said to you, "Cause it to make a piece of land that amounts to 100 square cubits that is round"—what is the diameter?

    Answer: 11.28 cubits

12. A rectangular plot of land is 60 cubits square, the diagonal being 13 cubits. Now how many cubits does it take to make a side?

    Answer: The rectangle has sides 5 cubits and 12 cubits.

13. Given a pyramid 300 cubits high, with a square base 500 cubits to a side, determine the distance from the center of any side to the apex.

    Answer: 390.51 cubits

14. Given a circular conduit 100 cubits in length, 3 cubits in diameter at its foot, and 1 cubit in diameter at its top, determine its volume.

    Answer: 340.34 cubits^3

15. Find the height of a square pyramid with a *seked* of 5 hands and 1 finger per cubit and a base 140 cubits on a side.
    [*Note:* The Egyptians measured the steepness of the face of a pyramid by forming a ratio of "run" to "rise," that is, by giving the horizontal departure of the oblique face from the vertical for each unit of height. The vertical unit was taken as the cubit and the horizontal unit as a hand, where there were seven hands to a cubit and five fingers to a hand. The Egyptian ratio of run to rise was called the *seked*.]

    Answer: 94.23 cubits

Michigan Papyrus (A.D. 150): *A Greco-Egyptian papyrus obtained by Professor Francis Kelsey of the University of Michigan in 1921. The papyrus contains three algebraic problems and illustrates the high level of problem-solving demonstrated in Egypt at this time.*

16. Given four numbers, their sum is 9,900, let the second exceed the first by $\frac{1}{7}$ the first, let the third exceed the sum of the first two by 300, and let the fourth exceed the sum of the first three by 300. Find the numbers.

    Answer: 1,050, 1,200, 2,550, 5,100

17. Given: a circle with an inscribed equilateral triangle. The triangle has an area of 12 square units. What is the area of the circle?

     Answer: 29.02 square units

18. A measure of cloth that is 7 cubits in height and 5 cubits in width amounts to 35 cloth cubits. Take off 1 cubit from its height and add it to the width so that the area remains the same. What measurement is added to its width?

     Answer: $\frac{5}{6}$ cubit

Babylonia

Tablet collections (2000–1000 B.C.): *Thousands of Babylonian clay tablets have been discovered. Most have been unearthed at the sites of the ancient cities of Nippur and Susa. About 400 of these tablets are known to contain mathematical material, but few have been deciphered. Major collections of such tablets are found at the Louvre museum in Paris and at Yale University, Columbia University, and the University of Pennsylvania in the United States.*

(*Note:* For computational ease, numbers originally given in sexagesimal form [i.e., base 60] have been converted here to base 10. To preserve historical interest, some Babylonian units of measure are retained, usually in a self-explanatory manner. As an added facet of historical interest, Babylonian algebraic-geometric terminology is presented in several problems: An unknown was perceived as the length of a line; a product of two unknowns, the area of a rectangle or, when appropriate, a square. Contemporary student problem-solvers will have to "translate" the Babylonian terminology to present-day algebraic form and proceed accordingly.)

1. I have added the area and two thirds the side of my square, and it is $\frac{35}{60}$. What is the side of the square?

     Answer: $\frac{1}{2}$ unit

2. I have a reed. I know not its dimension. I broke off from it 1 cubit and walked 60 times along the length. I restored to it what I had broken off, then walked 30 times along its length. The area is 375 square cubits. What was the original length of the reed?

     Answer: 1.177 cubits

3. I found a stone but did not weigh it: after I added to it $\frac{1}{7}$ of its weight and then $\frac{1}{11}$ of this new weight, I weighed the total at 1 *mina*. What was the original weight of the stone? Scribe's answer: The original weight was $\frac{2}{3}$ *mina*, 8 *sheqels*, and $22\frac{1}{2}$ *se*. [If 1 *mina* = 60 *sheqels* and 1 *sheqel* = 180 *se*, verify the correctness of the scribe's answer.]

     Answer: 48.125 *sheqels*; the scribe is correct!

4. I have added 7 times the side of my square of 11 times its surface to obtain 6.25 units. Reckon with 7 and 11. [Find the side of the square.]

     Answer: $\frac{1}{2}$ unit

5. There are two silver rings; $\frac{1}{7}$ of the first and $\frac{1}{11}$ of the second ring are broken off, so that what is broken off weighs 1 *sheqel*. The first diminished by its $\frac{1}{7}$ weighs as much as the second diminished by its $\frac{1}{11}$. What did the silver rings originally weigh?

   Answer: 4.375 *sheqels* and 4.125 *sheqels*

6. I found a stone but did not weigh it; after I subtracted one seventh and then subtracted one thirteenth [of the remainder], I weighed it at 1 *mana*. What was the original weight of the stone? [1 *mana* = 60 *sheqels*]

   Answer: 1 *mana*, 15.833 *sheqels*

7. I found a stone but did not weigh it; after I weighed out 6 times its weight and added 2 *sheqels*, I then added one third of one seventh of this amount multiplied by 24; the weight was then 1 *mana*. What was the original weight? [1 *mana* = 60 *sheqels*]

   Answer: 4.33 *sheqels*

8. I have two fields of grain. From the first field I harvest $\frac{2}{3}$ a bushel of grain/unit area; from the second, $\frac{1}{2}$ bushel/unit area. The yield of the first field exceeds the second by 50 bushels. The total area of the two fields together is 300 sq. units. What is the area of each field?

   Answer: 171.428 sq. units, 128.57 sq. units

9. I have multiplied length and width, obtaining the area. Then I added to the area the excess of length over width and obtained the result 183. Further, when I added the length and width, I obtained 27. Find the length, width, and area.

   Answer: 15 units, 12 units, 180 sq. units, *or* 14 units, 13 units, 182 sq. units

10. A little [rectangular] canal is to be excavated for a length of 5 kilometers. Its width is 2 meters and its depth 1 meter. Each laborer is assigned to remove 4 cubic meters of earth, for which he will be paid $\frac{1}{3}$ basket of barley. How many laborers are required for the job, and what are the total wages to be paid?

    Answer: 2,500 laborers, $833\frac{1}{3}$ baskets of grain

11. It is known that the digging of a canal becomes more difficult the deeper one goes. In order to compensate for this fact, differential work allotments were computed: A laborer working at the top level was expected to remove $\frac{1}{3}$ *sar* of earth in one day, while a laborer at the middle level removed $\frac{1}{6}$ *sar* and one at the bottom level, $\frac{1}{9}$ *sar*. If a fixed amount of earth is to be removed from a canal in one day, how much digging time should be spent at each level?

    Answer: top level, $\frac{1}{6}$ day; middle level, $\frac{1}{3}$ day; bottom, $\frac{1}{2}$ day

12. A little canal is 5 *kus* in length, has an upper width of [b_u] of 3 *kus* and lower width b_l of 2 *kus* and a depth of 2 *kus*. What is the inclination of the wall per 1 *kus* depth? [Refer to diagram.]

    Answer: $\frac{1}{2}$ *kus*

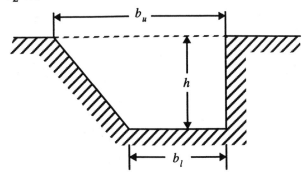

13. A triangular piece of land is divided among 6 brothers by equidistant lines constructed perpendicular to the base of the triangle. The length of the base is 390 units, and the area of the triangle is 40,950 sq. units. What is the difference in area between adjacent plots of land?

    Answer: 2,275 sq. units

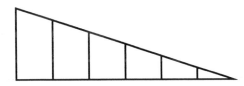

14. *Given:* trapezoid *ABCD* where *AB* ∥ *CD*. Let *EF* be constructed parallel to *AB* so that area *BEFA* = 843.75 sq. units, area *ECDF* = 2,531.25 sq. units, *AF* = $\frac{1}{5}$ *FD*, and *EF* = 52.5. Find the lengths *AB*, *CD*, *AF*, and *FD*.

    Answer: *AB* = 60, *CD* = 15, *AF* = 15, *FD* = 75

China

Nine Chapters on the Mathematical Arts (ca. **100** B.C.): *A collection of 246 problems and their solutions. The problems all pertain to the bureaucratic needs of the Chinese empire and concern such topics as the distribution of grain, the collection of taxes, and the construction of dikes and fortifications. The problems are divided into nine chapters, with each chapter focusing on a specific application.*

1. A cow, a horse, and a goat were in a wheat field and consumed some stalks of wheat. Damages of 5 baskets of grain were asked by the wheat field's owner. If the goat ate one half the number of stalks as the horse, and the horse ate one half of what was eaten by the cow, how much should be paid by the owners of the goat, horse, and cow, respectively?

    Answer: cow, $2\frac{6}{7}$ baskets; horse, $1\frac{3}{7}$ baskets; goat, $\frac{5}{7}$ basket

2. A certain number of people are buying some chickens. If each person pays 9 coins, there is a surplus of 11 coins, and if each person pays 6 coins, there is a deficiency of 16 coins. Find the number of people and the cost of the chickens.

    Answer: 9 people; 70 coins

3. *Given:* a wooden log of diameter 2 feet 5 inches from which a 7-inch-thick board is to be cut. What is the maximum possible width of the board?

    Answer: 28.142 inches

4. A tree is 20 feet tall and has a circumference of 3 feet. There is a vine that winds seven equally spaced times around the tree and reaches to the top. What is the length of the vine?

    Answer: 29 feet

5. Three sheafs of good crop, 2 sheafs of mediocre crop, and 1 sheaf of a poor crop produce 39 *dou* of grain. Two sheafs of good, 3 of mediocre, and 1 of poor produce 34 *dou*. One sheaf of good, 2 of mediocre, and 3 of poor produce 26 *dou*. What is the yield for one sheaf of good crop? one of mediocre crop? one of poor crop? [*dou* = 10.3 liters]

    Answer: good, $9\frac{1}{4}$; medium, $4\frac{1}{4}$; poor, $2\frac{3}{4}$

6. A man who had stolen a horse rode away on its back. When the thief had gone 37 *li* (miles), the owner discovered the theft and pursued the thief for 145 *li*. The owner then returned, being unable to overtake the thief. When the owner turned back, the thief was riding 23 *li* ahead of him; if the owner had continued his pursuit without coming back, in how many miles would he have overtaken the thief?

    Answer: 385 miles

7. Four countries are required to furnish wagons to transport 250,000 *hu* of grain to a depot. There are 10,000 families in the first county, which is 8 days' travel to the depot; 9,500 families in the second county, which is 10 days' travel; 12,350 families in the third county, 13 days' distant; and 12,200 families in the last county, which is 20 days' travel to the depot. The total number of wagons required is 1,000. How many wagons are to be provided by each county according to the size of its population and the distance from the depot?
    [*Note:* 1 *hu* = 10 *dou*. Let the number of wagons supplied be directly proportional to population size and inversely proportional to distance from the depot.]

    Answer: 332, 253, 253, 162 respectively

8. A square-walled city of unknown dimensions has four gates, one at the center of each side. A tree stands 20 *pu* from the north gate. One must walk 14 *pu* southward from the south gate and then turn west and walk 1,775 *pu* before he can see the tree. What are the dimensions of the city?

    Answer: Each side is 250 *pu* long.

9. Two men starting from the same point begin walking in different directions. Their rates of travel are in the ratio 7:3. The slower man walks toward the east. His faster compan-

ion walks to the south a distance of 10 *pu* and then turns toward an intercept course and proceeds until both men meet. How many *pu* did each man walk?

> *Answer:* slow walker, 10.5 *pu*; fast walker, 24.5 *pu*

10. A hill lies west of a tree whose height is 95 *ch'ih*. The distance between the hill and the tree is known to be 53 *li*. A man 7 *ch'ih* tall stands 3 *li* east of the tree. If the tops of the hill and the tree are aligned in the path of the man's vision, what is the height of the hill? [1 *li* = 1,500 *ch'ih*]

> *Answer:* 1,649.66 *ch'ih*

11. Of two water reeds, the one grows 3 feet and the other 1 foot on the first day. The growth of the first becomes every day half of that of the preceding day, while the other grows twice as much as on the day before. In how many days will the two grow to equal heights?

> *Answer:* 2.5 days

The Sea Island Mathematical Manual (A.D. 263): *Written by the mathematician Liu Hui as a supplement to the* Nine Chapters. *This collection of nine surveying problems eventually became a separate mathematical classic.*

12. Now for [the purpose of] looking at a distant sea island, erect two poles of the same height, 3 *chang* [on the ground], the distance between the poles being 1,000 *pu*. Assume that the rear and front poles are aligned with the island. By moving 123 *pu* back from the front pole and observing the peak of the island from ground level, it is noticed that the tip of the front pole coincides with the peak. Then by moving 127 *pu* back from the rear pole and observing the peak of the island from ground level again, the top of the back pole also coincides with the peak. What is the height of the island, and how far is it from the front pole? [1 *li* = 300 *pu* = 180 *chang*]

> *Answer:* The height of the island is 4 *li* 55 *pu*; it is 102 *li* 150 *pu* from the front pole.

Precious Mirror of the Four Elements (A.D. 1303): *A text compiled by the mathematician Zhu Shijie. It features a technique called the "celestial element method," which was used to solve higher-order algebraic equations. This book marks the high point of the development of traditional Chinese algebra.*

13. Now there is a square pond [with vertical banks]; each side is 10 feet long. Reeds grow vertically along the western bank and reach exactly 3 feet out of the water. On the eastern bank another kind of reed grows exactly 1 foot out of the water. When the two reeds are made to meet, they [their tops] are exactly level with the water surface. Permit me to ask how to determine these three things; the depth of the water and the length of each reed?

> *Answer:* The pond is 5.6 feet deep; the reeds are 8.6 feet and 6.6 feet long respectively.

14. I take along a bottle with some wine in it for an excursion in the spring. On reaching a tavern, I double the bottle's contents and drink 1⁹⁄₁₀ *dou* in the tavern. After passing 4

taverns, the bottle is empty. Permit me to ask how much wine was there at the beginning?

Answer: 1.78125 *dou*

Greece

Greek Anthology (A.D. 500): *A collection of 46 problems assembled by the grammarian Metrodorus. The problems are set in a witty or riddle form. This collection is sometimes called the* Palatine.

1. First speaker: Give me two *minas* and I become twice as much as you.
   Second speaker: And if I get the same from you, I am four times as much as you.
   How many *minas* does each person have?

   Answer: $3\frac{5}{7}$ *minas*; $4\frac{6}{7}$ *minas*

2. First person: I am equal to the second and one third of the third.
   Second person: I am equal to the third and one third of the first.
   Third person: And I to one third of the second plus ten.
   What is the value of each person?

   Answer: 45, 37.5, 22.5

3. This tomb holds Diophantus. Ah, how great a marvel! The tomb tells scientifically the measure of his life. God granted him to be a boy for the sixth part of his life, and adding a twelfth part to this, He clothed his cheeks with down. He lit him the light of the wedlock after a seventh part, and five years after his marriage, He granted him a son.

   Alas, late-born wretched child; after attaining the measure of half his father's life, chill Fate took him. After consoling his grief by this science of numbers for four years, he ended his life.

   [Determine the number of years for each respective event in the life of Diophantus.]

   Answer: Childhood, 14 years; youth, 7 years; married at 33 years; son born at 38 years; son dies, 80 years; grief, 4 years; Diophantus' age at death, 84 years.

4. Elder: Where have all the apples gone, my child?
   Child: Ino has two sixths and Semale one eighth, and Antonoe went off with one fourth, while Agave snatched from my bosom and carried away a fifth. For thee ten apples are left, but I, yes, I swear it by dear Cypris, have only this one.
   How many apples were there originally?

   Answer: 120 apples

5. Demochares has lived a fourth of his life as a boy, a fifth as a youth, and a third as a man, and has spent 13 years in his old age. How old is he?

   Answer: 60 years old

6. After staining the holy chaplet of fair-eyed Justice that I might see thee, all-subduing gold, grow so much, I have nothing; for I gave 40 talents under evil auspices to my

friends in vain, while, O ye varied mischances of men, I see my enemies in possession of the half, the third, and the eighth of my fortune. [How many talents did this unhappy man once own?]

Answer: 960 talents

7. The three Graces were carrying baskets of apples, and in each was the same number. The nine Muses met them and asked each for apples, and they gave the same number to each Muse and the 9 and the 3 each had the same number. Tell me how many they gave and how they all had the same number. [*Note:* This is an indeterminate problem—find the smallest correct solution.]

Answer: Each had 4n apples, gave away 3n, and kept n; let n = 1.
Then each Grace and each Muse was left with 1 apple.

8. Brickmaker, I am in a hurry to erect this house. Today is cloudless and I do not require many more bricks, for I have all I want but 300. Thou alone in 1 day couldst make as many, but thy son left off working when he had finished 200, and thy son-in-law when he had made 250. Working all together, in how many days can you make these?

Answer: $^2/_5$ day

9. I am a brazen lion; my spouts are my 2 eyes, my mouth, and the flat of my right foot. My right eye fills a jar in 2 days, my left eye in 3, and my foot in 4. My mouth is capable of filling it in 6 hours. Tell me how long all 4 together will take to fill it? [Assume 1 day = 12 hours.]

Answer: $^{144}/_{37}$ hours

10. Make a crown of gold, copper, tin, and iron weighing 60 *minae*: gold and copper shall be $^2/_3$ of it; gold and tin, $^3/_4$ of it; and gold and iron, $^3/_5$ of it. Find the required weights of gold, copper, tin, and iron.

Answer: 30.5 *minae* of gold; 9.5 *minae* of copper; 14.5 *minae* of tin; and 5.5 *minae* of iron

Europe

Propositions for Sharpening the Wits of the Young (A.D. **800**): *A collection of 53 puzzle-problems compiled by the monk Alcuin of York. This work was used as a text for youths in Charlemagne's court school.*

1. A king, recruiting his army, conscripts 1 man in the first town, 2 in the second, 4 in the third, 8 in the fourth, and so on, until he has taken men from 30 towns. How many men does he collect in all?

Answer: 1,073,741,823 men

2. A ladder has 100 steps. On the first step sits 1 pigeon; on the second, 2; on the third, 3; and so on up to the hundredth. How many pigeons in all?

Answer: 5,050

3. An old man met a child, "Good day, my son," he said, "may you live as long again as you have lived, and as long again, and thrice as much as the sum of the last two, and then if God gives you one year more, you will be just a century old." How old was the boy?

    Answer: 11 years

4. A dog chasing a rabbit, which has a start of 150 feet, jumps 9 feet every time the rabbit jumps 7. In how many leaps does the dog overtake the rabbit?

    Answer: 75 leaps

5. If 100 bushels of corn be distributed among 100 people in such a manner that each man receives 3 bushels, each woman 2, and each child $\frac{1}{2}$ bushel, how many men, women, and children were there?

    Answer: There are several possible solution sets. One such set is: 11 men, 15 women, and 74 children.

6. Thirty flasks—10 full, 10 half empty, and 10 completely empty—are to be divided among 3 sons so that flasks and contents should be shared equally. How may this be done?

    Answer: There are many ways to divide these flasks among the sons. One way is: The first and second sons each get 5 full and 5 empty flasks; the third son then gets 10 half-empty flasks.

7. A wolf, a goat, and a cabbage must be transported across a river in a boat holding only one besides the ferryman. How must he carry them across so that the goat shall not eat the cabbage, nor the wolf the goat?

    Answer: First take the goat across; return empty to fetch the cabbage. The cabbage is brought across and the goat returned and the wolf brought over. The ferry then returns empty finally to bring the goat across.

8. When a farmer goes plowing and has turned three times at each end of his field, how many furrows has he plowed?

    Answer: 7 furrows

9. Six laborers were hired to build a house. Five of these were experienced; one was a lad, an apprentice. The five men were to divide between them as payment 25 pence a day, less the payment made to the apprentice, which was to be half of what an experienced worker received. How much did each receive as daily wages?

    Answer: experienced worker, $4\frac{6}{11}$ pence; apprentice, $2\frac{3}{11}$ pence

10. Three men with one sister each were traveling together. They came to a river and were obliged to cross it by boat. The boat would hold only two people at a time. Ethics demands that no one of the women should cross the river alone with a man other than her brother. How may they proceed?

    Answer: Each brother takes his sister across the river, then returns to let the next brother take his sister across. When all the women are across, then the last brother must ferry the two waiting brothers to join their sisters.

India

***Lilavati* (ca. 1150):** *A text written by the mathematician–astronomer Bhāskara II and named after his daughter. This work is a summary of 500 years of Hindu mathematics tradition.*

1. Given: a vertical pole of height 12 feet. The ingenious man who can compute the length of the pole's shadows, the difference of which is known to be 19 feet, and the difference of the hypotenuses formed, 13 feet, I take to be thoroughly acquainted with the whole of algebra as well as arithmetic.

   Answer: $3\frac{1}{2}$ feet and $22\frac{1}{2}$ feet

2. The eighth part of a troop of monkeys, squared, was skipping in a grove and delighted with their sport. Twelve remaining [monkeys] were seen on the hill, amused with chattering to each other. How many were they in all?

   Answer: 16 or 48

3. A powerful, unvanquished, excellent black snake which is 80 *angulas* in length enters into a hole at the rate of $7\frac{1}{2}$ *angulas* in $\frac{5}{14}$ of a day, and in the course of a day its tail grows $1\frac{1}{4}$ of an *angula*. O ornament of arithmeticians, tell me by what time this serpent enters fully into the hole?

   Answer: 4.38 days

4. Of a collection of mango fruits, the king took $\frac{1}{6}$; the queen, $\frac{1}{5}$ of the remainder; and the three princes, $\frac{1}{4}$, $\frac{1}{3}$, and $\frac{1}{2}$ of the successive remainders; and the youngest child took the remaining three mangoes. O you who are clever in miscellaneous problems on fractions, give out the measure of that collection of mangoes.

   Answer: 18 mangoes

5. The mixed price of 9 citrons and 7 fragrant wood apples is 107; again, the mixed price of 7 citrons and 9 fragrant wood apples is 101. O you arithmetician, tell me quickly the price of a citron and of a wood apple here, having distinctly separated those prices well.

   Answer: citron, 8; wood apple, 5

6. One fourth of a herd of camels was seen in the forest; twice the square root of that herd had gone to the mountain slopes; and 3 times 5 camels remained on the riverbank. What is the numerical measure of that herd of camels?

   Answer: 36 camels

7. The sum of 390 was lent in 3 portions at interest of 5, 2, and 4, in the hundred; and amounted in 7, 10, and 5 months respectively to an equal amount on all three portions with the interest. Say the amount of the portions.

   Answer: 86, 152, 152 (answer rounded to nearest integer)

8. In an expedition to seize his enemy's elephants, a king marched 2 *yojanas* the first day. Say, intelligent calculator, with what increasing rate of daily march did he proceed, since he reached his foe's city, a distance of 80 *yojanas*, in a week?

    Answer: $22/7$ *yojanas*

9. A cat sitting on a wall 4 cubits high saw a rat prowling 8 cubits from the foot of the wall. The rat, too, perceived the puss and hastened towards its abode at the foot of the wall; but it was caught by the cat proceeding diagonally an equal distance. At what point within the 8 cubits was the rat caught?

    Answer: 3 cubits from the wall

10. The square root of half the number of bees in a swarm has flown out upon a jessamine bush; $8/9$ of the swarm has remained behind. A female bee flies about a male that is buzzing within a lotus flower into which he was allured in the night by its sweet odor, but is now imprisoned in it. Tell me, most enchanting lady, the number of bees.

    Answer: 72 bees

Islamic World

The Algebra of al-Khwarizmi **(ca. A.D. 820):** *This book was written by Muhammed ibn Musa al-Khwarizmi, a scholar at the House of Wisdom in Baghdad. It combined the mathematical knowledge of the Greeks with that of the Hindus in solving simple equations. Two processes were used: "balancing" and "restoring." In Arabic, "restoring" was called* al-jabr. *When the book reached Europe, it was translated into Latin and became the first "algebra" book in the West.*

1. A woman dies, leaving her husband, a son, and three daughters. Calculate the fraction of her estate each will receive.
   [*Note:* The conditions of Islamic law must be followed, namely, the husband must receive $1/4$ share and a son twice as much as a daughter.]

    Answer: husband $1/4$; son $3/10$; daughters $3/20$ each

2. A woman dies, leaving her husband, a son, and three daughters, but she also bequeaths to a stranger $1/8 + 1/7$ of the estate. Calculate the shares of each heir.
   [*Note:* Legacies outside of the family cannot exceed $1/3$ the estate unless natural heirs agree; other sharing conditions as above after the external legacy is paid.]

    Answer: husband, .183036; son, .219644; daughters, .109822 each

3. Given a triangular piece of land having two sides 10 yards in length and its base 12 yards, what is the largest square that can be constructed within this piece of land so that one of its sides lies along the base of the triangle?

    Answer: 4.8 yards

4. You have two sums of money, the difference of which is 2 *dirhams*; you divide the smaller sum by the larger and the quotient is equal to $1/2$. What are the two sums of money?

    Answer: 4 *dirhams* and 2 *dirhams*

The Algebra of Abu Kamil (ca. A.D. 900): *This book was written as a commentary upon al-Khwarizmi's algebra. Its contents strongly influenced the work of the European mathematician Fibonacci.*

5. One says that 10 garments were purchased by 2 men at a price of 72 *dirhams*. Each paid 36 *dirhams*. The garments are varied in value. The price of each garment of one man is 3 *dirhams* more than the price for each garment of the other. How many garments did each man buy?

    Answer: 6 and 4

6. Given a number, take $\frac{1}{3}$ of the number away from itself and add 2. If this result is multiplied by itself, it equals the number plus 24. What is the number?

    Answer: 5.0903

Italy

Liber Abaci (1200): *Written by the Italian mathematician Leonardo of Pisa, also known as Fibonacci ("the son of Bonaccio"). The book consisted of 15 chapters devoted to techniques of arithmetic and simple algebra. Its contents strongly advocated the use of Hindu-Arabic numerals. This work was very influential and had a great impact on European mathematics. It contained a large assortment of problems that were copied and reused for centuries.*

1. A certain lion could eat a sheep in 4 hours; a leopard could eat one in 5 hours; and a bear, in 6 hours. How many hours would it take for them to devour a sheep if it were thrown in among them?

    Answer: 1.62 hours

2. A certain man doing business in Lucca doubled his money there, and then spent 12 *denarii*. Thereupon, leaving, he went to Florence; there he also doubled his money and spent 12 *denarii*. Returning to Pisa, he there doubled his money and spent 12 *denarii*, nothing remaining. How much did he have in the beginning?

    Answer: $10\frac{1}{2}$ *denarii*

3. There were two men, of whom the first had 3 small loaves of bread and the other, 2. They walked to a spring, where they sat down and ate; and a soldier joined them and shared their meal, each of the three men eating the same amount; and when all the bread was eaten, the soldier departed, leaving 5 *bezants* to pay for his meal. The first man accepted 3 of these *bezants*, since he had had 3 loaves; the other took the remaining 2 *bezants* for his 2 loaves. Was the division fair?

    Answer: No! The man who gave 3 loaves should receive 4 *bezants*; the other man, 1 *bezant*.

4. A man whose end was approaching summoned his sons and said, "Divide my money as I shall prescribe." To his eldest son, he said, "You are to have 1 *bezant* and a seventh of what is left." To his second son he said, "Take 2 *bezants* and a seventh of what remains." To the third son, "You are to take 3 *bezants* and a seventh of what is left." Thus he gave

each son 1 *bezant* more than the previous son and a seventh of what remained, and to the last son all that was left. After following their father's instructions with care, the sons found that they had shared their inheritance equally. How many sons were there, and how large was the estate?

Answer: The estate was worth 36 *bezants*, and the man had 6 sons.

5. Three men having *denarii* found a purse of 23 *denarii*. The first man said to the second, "If I take this purse, I will have twice as much as you"; the second said to the third, "If I take the purse I will have three times as much as you"; and the third said to the first, "If I take the purse, I will have four times as much as you." How much did each one have?

Answer: 9, 16, and 13 *denarii* respectively

6. Two ants are 100 paces apart, crawling back and forth along the same path. The first goes $\frac{1}{3}$ pace forward a day and returns $\frac{1}{4}$ pace, the other goes forward $\frac{1}{5}$ pace and returns $\frac{1}{6}$ pace. How many days before the first ant overtakes the second?

Answer: 854 days

7. If A gets from B 7 *denarii*, then A's sum is fivefold B's; if B gets from A 5 *denarii*, then B's sum is sevenfold A's. How much has each?

Answer: A has $^{121}/_{17}$ *denarii*; B has $^{167}/_{17}$ *denarii*.

8. A certain king sent 30 men into his orchard to plant trees. If they could set out 1,000 trees in 9 days, in how many days would 36 men set out 4,400 trees?

Answer: 33 days

9. A man entered an orchard through 7 gates, and there took a certain number of apples. When he left the orchard, he gave the first guard half the apples he had and 1 apple more. To the second guard he gave half his remaining apples and 1 apple more. He did the same to each of the remaining five guards and left the orchard with 1 apple. How many apples did he gather in the orchard?

Answer: 382 apples

10. There is a lion in a well whose depth is 50 *palms*. He climbs $\frac{1}{7}$ of a *palm* daily and slips back $\frac{1}{9}$ of a *palm*. In how many days will he get out of the well?

Answer: 1,572 days

11. A man visited three fairs carrying with him $10\frac{1}{2}$ *denarii*. He doubled his money at each fair and also spent a certain same amount at each fair. He returned home with no money. How much did he spend at the fairs?

Answer: 12 *denarii* at each fair

12. There is a tree with 100 branches; each branch has 100 nests; each nest, 100 eggs; each egg, 100 birds. How many nests, eggs, and birds are there?

Answer: $(100)^2 = 10,000$ nests, $(100)^3 = 1,000,000$ eggs, $(100)^4 = 100,000,000$ birds

13. How many pairs of rabbits will be produced in a year, beginning with a single pair, if in every month each pair bears a new pair which becomes productive from the second month on?

    Answer: 233 pairs

14. A cistern can be filled by one pipe in one hour, by another in two, by a third in three, and by a fourth in four. How long will it take all four pipes to fill the cistern?

    Answer: approximately 29 minutes

15. A certain man invests 1 *denarius* at interest at such a rate that in 5 years he has 2 *denarii*, and in 5 years thereafter the money doubles. I ask how many *denarii* he would gain from this one *denarius* in 100 years?

    Answer: 1,048,576 *denarii*

16. A certain man says he can weigh any amount from 1 to 40 pounds using only 4 weights. What size must they be?

    Answer: 1, 3, 9, 27

Treviso Arithmetic (1478): *The first printed arithmetic book in Europe. Its author, a reckoning master, remains unknown, so it is named after the city in which it was published. The book's contents focus on problems of commercial arithmetic that concern such topics as partnership, discounting, and the exchange of money.*

17. When a bushel of wheat is worth 8 *lire*, the bakers make a loaf of bread weighing 6 ounces. Required: the number of ounces in the weight of a loaf when it is worth 5 *lire* a bushel.

    Answer: $9\frac{3}{5}$ ounces

18. If 1,000 pounds of pepper are worth 80 *ducats*, 16 *grossi* and $\frac{1}{4}$, what will 9,917 pounds and $\frac{1}{2}$ be worth? [1 *ducat* = 24 *grossi*]

    Answer: 800 *ducats*, 2.76 *grossi*

19. Three men—Tomasso, Domenego, and Nicolo—entered into partnership. Tomasso put in 760 *ducats* on the first day of January 1472 and on the first day of April took out 200 *ducats*. Domenego put in 616 *ducats* on the first day of February 1472 and on the first day of June took out 96 *ducats*. Nicolo put in 892 *ducats* on the first day of February 1472 and on the first day of March took out 252 *ducats*. And on the first day of January 1475, they found that they had gained 3,168 *ducats*, 13 *grossi* and $\frac{1}{2}$. Required: the share of each, so that no one shall be cheated.

    Answer: Tomasso: 1,052 *ducats*, 11.273 *grossi*
    Domenego: 942 *ducats*, 3.674 *grossi*
    Nicolo: 1,173 *ducats*, 22.55 *grossi*

20. A carpenter has undertaken to build a house in 20 days. He takes on another man and says: "If we build the house together, we can accomplish the work in 8 days!" Required: to know how long it would take this other man to build the house alone.

    Answer: 13 $\frac{1}{3}$ days

Ars Magna **(1545):** *This was the first great Latin algebra book of the Renaissance. In English its title is* The Great Art. *This book was written by Girolamo Cardano (1501–1576), a mysterious character in the history of mathematics. Among its innovations, the book included solution methods for solving cubic equations, a recognition of negative roots for an equation, and computations with imaginary numbers.*

21. There were two leaders, each of whom divided 48 *aurei* among his soldiers. One of these had two more *aurei* for each soldier than the other. The one who had two soldiers fewer had four *aurei* more for each soldier. Find how many soldiers each had.

    Answer: 12 and 8

22. The dowry of Francis's wife is 100 *aurei* more than Francis's own property is worth, and the square of the dowry is 400 more than the square of his property's value. Find the dowry and the property value.

    Answer: dowry, 52 *aurei*; property value, 48 *aurei*

23. An oracle ordered a prince to build a sacred building whose space would be 400 cubits, the length being 6 cubits more than the width, and the width 3 cubits more than the height. Find the dimensions of the building.

    Answer: height, 4.20 cubits; width, 7.20 cubits; length, 13.20 cubits

Miscellaneous Problems from Renaissance Europe

The majority of mathematical problems found in the texts of this time concerned trade and commerce. Their contents provide a good picture of the business world at this time.

1. A merchant gives his factor 1,200 *florins*; the factor contributes 500 *florins* of his own and his services and gets $\frac{2}{5}$ of the profits. How high are the factor's services estimated?

   Answer: 300 *florins*

2. Suppose I tell you that I bought saffron in Siena for 18 *lire* a pound and took it to Venice, when I found that 10 ounces Siena weight are equivalent to 12 ounces in Venice, and 10 *lire* in Siena are equal to 8 *lire* in Venice, and I sold the saffron for 14 *lire* of Venetian money a pound. I ask how much I gained percent?

   Answer: 12% profit

3. A man has four creditors. To the first he owes 624 *ducats*; to the second, 546; to the third, 492; and to the fourth, 368. It happened that the man defaulted and escaped; his creditors found that his goods amounted to 830 *ducats* in all. In what ratio should they divide this, and what will be the share of each?

   Answer: ratio, 3.07:2.69:2.42:1.81; shares, 254.81, 223.27, 200.86, 150.23 ducats respectively

4. Suppose you have two sorts of wine. A measure of the poorer sort is worth 6 *denarii*. One of the better sort is worth 13 *denarii*. I wish to have a measure of mixed wine worth 8 *denarii*. [How much of each wine do I put in the mixture?]

   Answer: 5 measures of cheap wine with 2 measures of expensive wine

5. Two men rent a pasture for 100 *lires* on the understanding that two cows are to be counted as being equivalent to three sheep. The first puts in 60 cows and 85 sheep; the second, 80 cows and 100 sheep. How much should each pay?

    Answer: 44.3 *lires* and 55.7 *lires* respectively

6. Two wine merchants enter Paris, one of them with 64 casks of wine, the other with 20. Since they have not enough money to pay the custom duties, the first pays 5 casks of wine and 40 *francs*, and the second pays 2 casks of wine and receives 40 *francs* in change. What is the price of each cask of wine and the duty on it?

    Answer: price of each cask, 120 *francs*; duty, 10 *francs*/cask

7. The radius of the inscribed circle of a triangle is 4, and the segments into which one side is divided by the point of contact are 6 and 8. Determine the other two sides.

    Answer: 15 and 13

8. A merchant bought 50,000 pounds of pepper in Portugal for 10,000 *scudi*, paying a tax of 500 *scudi*. He carried the pepper to Italy at a cost of 300 *scudi* and there paid another duty of 200 *scudi*. The transportation from the coast to Florence cost 100 *scudi*, and he was obliged to pay an impost of 100 *scudi* to that city. Lastly, the government demanded a tax from each merchant of 1,000 *scudi*. Now he is perplexed to know what price to charge per pound so that, after all these expenses, he may make a profit of $^1/_{10}$ of a *scudi* a pound.

    Answer: .344 *scudi*/pound

9. A man bought a number of bales of wool in London; each bale weighed 200 pounds, English measure, and each bale cost him 24 *fl*. He sent the wool to Florence and paid carriage duties and other expenses amounting to 10 *fl*. a bale. He wishes to sell the wool in Florence at such a price as to make 20 percent on his investment. How much should he charge a hundredweight if 100 London pounds are equivalent to 133 Florentine pounds?

    Answer: 15.34 *fl*/hundredweight

10. A merchant gave a university 2,814 *ducats* on the understanding that he was to be paid back 618 *ducats* a year for 9 years, at the end of which the 2,814 *ducats* should be considered as paid. What compound interest was he getting on his money?

    Answer: 16%+

America

***Hodder's Arithmetick* (1661):** *A standard British arithmetic that was adopted by the early colonies.*

1. A merchant oweth 500 £ to be paid in payments of 300 £ at 4 months, 100 £ at 6 months, and 100 £ at 12 months. The debtor agrees to discharge the whole debt in one payment. Now the question is, at what time the payment ought to be made, without damage unto the debtor or creditor. The creditor agrees to pay 6 percent per annum.

    Answer: 6 months

***Pike's A New and Complete System of Arithmetic* (1788):** *One of the first arithmetics written in the American Colonies.*

2. A, B, C bought a drove of sheep in company; A paid £14 5s.; B, £13 l0s.; and C, £1 5s. They agreed to sell the sheep so that each man got l8s. as pay for time, and the remainder should be divided in proportion to their several flocks. At the close of the sale they found themselves possessed of £46 5s. What was each man's gain exclusive of pay for time? [£1 = 20s.]

    Answer: A, £428; B, £405 9s.; C, £37 11s.

***The Principles of Arithmetic* (1856):** *A standard arithmetic of the times, written by Joseph Ray.*

3. Sold a consignment of pork and invested the proceeds in brandy, after deducting my commission, 4% for selling and $1\frac{1}{4}$% for buying; the brandy cost $2,304. What did the pork sell for, and what were my commissions?

    Answer: pork's price, $2,430; commissions, $126

4. I owe a man the following notes: one of $800 due May 16; one of $660 due July 1; one of $940 due Sept. 29. He wishes to exchange them for two notes of $1,200 each and wants one to fall due June 1. When should the other be due?

    Answer: September 9

5. What quantities of tea at 25¢ and 35¢ a pound, with 14 lbs. at 30¢ and 20 lbs. at 50¢ and 6 lbs. at 60¢, will make 56 lbs. at 40¢ a pound?

    Answer: 9 lbs. 9.6 oz. of 25¢ tea; 6 lb 6.4 oz. of 35¢ tea

6. A father left $20,000 to be divided among his four sons ages 6, 8, 10, and 12 years respectively so that each share placed at $4\frac{1}{2}$% compounded interest should amount to the same value when its possessor becomes of age 21. What were the amounts of each share?

    Answer: $4,360, $4,760, $5,200, $5,680 respectively

7. For every 8 sheep a farmer keeps, he plows 1 acre of land; and he keeps 1 acre of pasture for every 5 sheep. How many sheep can he keep on 325 acres?

    Answer: 1,000 sheep

***The New Normal Mental Arithmetic* (1873):** *Written by Edward Brooks, principal and professor of mathematics at the Pennsylvania State Normal School, now known as Millersville University, in Millersville, Pennsylvania. The Brooks series of arithmetics were widely used in Pennsylvania and Maryland during the second half of the 19th century. Their contents frequently reflect the agricultural nature of the region.*

8. Suppose that for every 4 cows a farmer has, he should plow 1 acre of land, and allow 1 acre of pasture for every 3 cows; how many cows could he keep on 140 acres?

    Answer: 240 cows

9. A gentleman received $4 a day for his labor and pays $8 a week for his board; at the expiration of 10 weeks he has saved $144. Required: the number of idle and working days.

   Answer: 14 idle days; 56 workdays

10. The head of a fish is 10 inches long, the tail is as long as the head plus $\frac{1}{2}$ of the body, and the body is as long as the head and tail both. Required: the length of the fish.

    Answer: 80 inches

11. If 5 pints of milk cost 12 cents, how many pints can you purchase for 25 cents?

    Answer: $10^5/_{12}$ pints

12. If I pay $1.60 for a bushel of blackberries, how much is a quart?

    Answer: $.05

England

***A Treatise of Arithmetic* (1880):** *A standard British text of the time, written by J. Hamblin Smith. The problem situations provide insights into Victorian life.*

1. If 12 horses can plow 96 acres in 6 days, how many horses will plow 64 acres in 8 days?

   Answer: 6 horses

2. If 44 cannon firing 30 rounds/hour for 3 hours a day consume 300 barrels of powder in 5 days, how long will 400 barrels last 66 cannon firing 40 rounds/hour for 5 hours a day?

   Answer: 2 days

3. A starts a business with a capital of £2,400 on the 19th of March, and on the 17th of July admits a partner, B, with a capital of £1,800. The profits amount to £943 by the 31st of December. What is each person's share?

   Answer: £659.29 and £283.71

4. The number of disposable seamen at Portsmouth is 800; at Plymouth, 756; and at Sheerness, 404. A ship is commissioned whose complement is 490 seamen. How many must be drafted from each place so as to take an equal proportion?

   Answer: Portsmouth, 200; Plymouth, 189; Sheerness, 101

Ein new Visier büchlein/

welches innhelt/wie man durch den Quadraten auff eynes yeden lands Eich/ein Rütten zübereyten/vñ damit yetlichs vnbekants vaß Visieren/vnd solches innhalt erkennen sol/Auffs new gebessert vnd gemert.

Title page of 15th-century arithmetic book.
What kind of mathematics does the illustration suggest?

CHAPTER 5

Activities for the Classroom

Of all the strategies for introducing a historical perspective into the teaching of mathematics, the one I favor personally the most is the use of historically based activities. Such activities can be class-oriented, that is, a single activity undertaken by the class as a whole; intended for small-group interactions when perhaps several activities can be undertaken simultaneously within the same class; or individually prescribed where single students undertake individual activities, either in class or as a homework assignment. Activities can, of course, be teacher-led and guided, and while some teaching situations may require this approach, a greater teaching flexibility and learning impact can be achieved through the use of self-contained and self-directed learning tasks.

A convenient form through which a historical learning task can be presented to students is a prepared packet or module consisting of several pages of informational, motivational, and directional text focused around a particular historical event or problem. These packets or modules can be designated by several different names. Each name, in a sense, emphasizes the essence of the learning experience: The terms *learning task* and *learning activity* imply that learning will take place by doing—a task is to be undertaken or an activity conducted. Still another popular term for these learning encounters is *experiment*, which carries with it a sense of exploring the unknown and arriving at discoveries. Throughout the remaining discussion, I refer to such teaching devices as *historical learning tasks (HLT)*.

While isolated historical learning tasks may occasionally appear among commercially produced learning/teaching materials, to my knowledge no complete set of such tasks is currently available. Most HLT's are teacher-designed and -produced. Twenty-one sample HLT's are presented in the following pages. They are included for illustrative purposes, classroom use, and possible adaptation. (See the Descriptive Listing that follows.) These HLT's have been designed to illustrate different instructional venues within the strategy of using learning tasks, to cater to different learning levels, and to demonstrate possible association of historical ideas with various mathematical disciplines, such as geometry and algebra.

Descriptive Listing of Historical Learning Tasks

No.	Name	Mathematical Emphasis (instructional level)*	Historical Topic
1	Figure It Out!	Algebra (II)	Figurative numbers
2	Piling Up Blocks	Geometry (general math)	Egyptian pyramid
3	Building Up Volume	Geometry, Algebra (I)	Dissection proofs
4	A Babylonian Discovery	Algebra (I), Computing	Babylonian computation
5	Picking Up the Pieces	Algebra (I)	Geometric algebra
6	Algebra with Lines	Algebra (II), Geometry	Ruler & compass construction
7	The Platonic Solids	Solid Geometry	Platonic solids, Euler's formula
8	The Golden Mean	Geometry, Algebra (I)	Golden ratio
9	The Bridge of Fools	Geometry	Proof in geometry
10	Decimal Mysteries	Computation (general math)	Decimal fractions
11	Medieval Multiplication	Computation (general math)	Multiplication algorithms
12	Rabdologia	Computing (general math)	Napier's bones
13	Pi Is . . .	Mathematical Approximation	Estimation of π
14	Shadow Reckoning	Geometry	Thales' geometry
15	Measuring the World	Trigonometry	Eratosthenes' measurement
16	Measuring Angles	Trigonometry	Early surveying
17	The *Lo Shu*	Computation (general math)	Magic square
18	Squaring the Circle	Geometry, Algebra (II)	Classical Greek problems
19	Regular Polygons	Geometry	Construction of polygons
20	Pascal's Triangle	Algebra (II)	Pascal's triangle
21	The Bridges of Koenigsberg	Computation (general math)	Euler's work in graph theory

*Indicates minimum level

If you would like to develop your own historical learning tasks, I have some advice. Ideally, an HLT should be self-contained and simply written. Keep exposition to a minimum and the vocabulary simple. Build each learning task around specific cognitive and/or affective objectives; its sequence of instructions and questions should guide the learners toward the desired objectives. In undertaking the task, students should practice their mathematical skills, learn something about mathematics and, through a historical approach, also learn something about how and why mathematics is done. The historical topic you choose for inclusion in a task should be interesting and within the capacity of student appreciation. For example, HLT's 1 and 2, "Figure It Out!" and "Piling Up Blocks," employ figurative numbers and the geometry of a pyramid to illustrate the use of inductive reasoning in the formulation of mathematical theories. "Rabdologia" (HLT 12) and "A Babylonian Discovery" (HLT 4) supply an understanding of algorithms and computing devices. In these exercises, students are required to compute in unfamiliar but purposeful ways and are encouraged to think further about the common algorithms they presently use. HLT 8, "The Golden Mean," attempts to entice its readers into the mysteries of the golden ratio and can serve as an enrichment activity. Similarly, "The Bridges of Koenigsberg" (HLT 21) introduces the students to some basic concepts of graph theory and network analysis, very broad-based enrichment topics.

The most essential aspect of an HLT is that it should require a doing of mathematics, an exploration of hypothesis, and a discovery of results. It should not be merely another form of a pencil-and-paper exercise. If possible, students should work together on the task, use the tools of modern mathematics (calculators and microcomputers) when appropriate, discuss procedures and results, and mutually agree on conclusions. This is a healthy and desirable learning situation. Some tasks may be open-ended, allowing for several answers and prompting a discussion as to the most acceptable (useful) answer. Such a situation might evolve from an estimation of π, HLT 13, "Pi Is . . . ." In many cases the activity undertaken by the student learner approximates the actual historical activity, as in "Measuring the World" (HLT 15).

In designing learning tasks, be creative and enliven your text with appropriate and appealing illustrations, attention-getters such as facsimiles of historical writings, pictures, or devices. You can even ask students in the task to use these historical materials in their investigations, as in HLT 5, "Picking Up the Pieces," and HLT 9, "The Bridge of Fools." You can find illustrations in various books on the history of mathematics or, if you are artistic, you can draw them yourself.

By engaging in the following tasks, students will learn not only something about mathematics but also something about how mathematics is done.

HLT 1

Figure It Out!

Have you ever heard the expression "She is good at figures" and wondered where it came from? It means that someone is good at working with numbers—doing computation. But how does the word *figure* come to convey the concept of "number"? The ancient Pythagoreans were obsessed with the concept of number; for them "all was number." They sought mystical meanings in number and manipulated them in various ways. One such way was to view a number geometrically, that is, to construct a geometric array of dots whose sum total represented a number. For example, an array made up of ten dots would represent the number 10, and then if this array was formed into a special geometrical figure, this figure would be associated with the number. Today these numbers are called polygonal or figurate numbers—numbers associated with a geometric figure.

Consider two classes of figurative numbers: the triangular numbers, represented by a triangle of dots, and the square numbers, represented by a square composed of dots.

In the following activities, triangular numbers are represented as T_n, where n indicates the order of the number. For example, T_3 is the third triangular number. Similarly, S_n is used to represent square numbers. On the last page of this activity, the first three triangular and square numbers are shown:

$$T_1 = 1, T_2 = 3, T_3 = 6$$

$$S_1 = 1, S_2 = 4, S_3 = 9$$

Name _____ Date _____

1. Continue constructing the next few triangular and square numbers. Using your diagram:

    a. List the first six triangular numbers.

    b. List the first six square numbers.

2. Let T_n = the nth triangular number.

    Confirm that $T_n = T_{n-1} + n$, where n = number of dots added.

    Thus:

    $$T_n = T_{n-1} + n$$
    $$= T_{n-2} + (n-1) + n$$

    •

    •

    •

    Generalize the result of this process to find a statement or an algebraic formula that describes the value of any T_n given the value for n, that is, find:

    $$T_n = f(n)$$

    (*Hint:* Draw a rectangle made up of two triangular numbers of the same size. What is the total number of dots in your rectangle?)

3. Let S_n = nth square number, so $S_n = n^2$ for all n. Geometrically verify the fact that $S_n = T_n + T_{n-1}$, that every square number can be represented as the sum of two triangular numbers. Use the results you found in step 2 above to develop an algebraic expression for this relationship.

4. In viewing a figurative number, you can find many geometric patterns. Often you can use these patterns to develop useful mathematical relationships. Consider a pattern found in a square number.

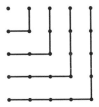

    The number represented by each L configuration is an odd number. Use this pattern to find the sum of n consecutive odd positive integers.

5. The Hindu mathematician Aryabhata I (ca. A.D. 500) developed a formula for the sum of the triangular numbers:

$$T_1 + T_2 + T_3 + \ldots + T_n = \frac{n\,(n+1)\,(n+2)}{6}$$

Use your knowledge of triangular numbers and their properties to verify this formula.

6. The Greek mathematician Archimedes (287–212 B.C.) developed a formula for the sum of the square numbers:

$$S_1 + S_2 + S_3 + \ldots + S_n = \frac{n\,(n+1)\,(2n+1)}{6}$$

Verify this formula.

Figure It Out!—Teacher's Guide

Mathematical learning objective: pattern recognition; practice in inductive reasoning

Materials needed: large-grid graph paper

Notes and suggestions: The illustration is taken from a Greek vase of about 500 B.C. It shows a man doing calculations using a computing board and table. Remember that the Greeks used letters of their alphabet for numbers, so the figures on the table are really numbers.

    This is a doodling activity. Encourage students to draw out figurative numbers and to explore their properties graphically. Solutions for the exercises can all be found in this manner.

1. a. 1, 3, 6, 10, 15, 21

   b. 1, 4, 9, 16, 25, 36

2. By constructing a few triangular numbers, the students should realize the property that $T_n = T_{n-1} + n$; however, it can be made clearer by use of a diagram:

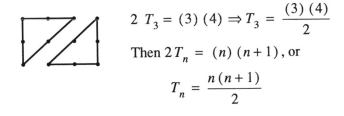

$$T_1 = 1 \quad +2 = T_2 \qquad T_2 = 3 \quad +3 = T_3$$

Generalizing the expression for T_n should show that T_n = the sum of the first n natural numbers:

$$T_3 = 1 + 2 + 3 = 6$$
$$T_8 = 1 + 2 + 3 + 4 + 5 + 6 + 7 + 8 = 36$$

Using the hint with two T_3's, a rectangle can be formed:

$$2\,T_3 = (3)\,(4) \Rightarrow T_3 = \frac{(3)\,(4)}{2}$$

Then $2\,T_n = (n)\,(n+1)$, or

$$T_n = \frac{n\,(n+1)}{2}$$

3.

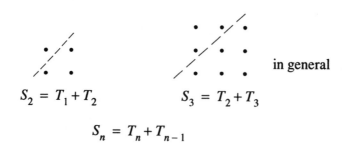

$$S_2 = T_1 + T_2 \qquad\qquad S_3 = T_2 + T_3 \qquad \text{in general}$$

$$S_n = T_n + T_{n-1}$$

Therefore, by the results in step 2:

$$S_n = \frac{n(n+1)}{2} + \frac{(n-1)n}{2} = n^2$$

4. For the pattern shown, we find $1 + 3 + 5 + 7 + 9 = (5)^2 = 25$. Therefore, the sum of the first n consecutive odd integers will be:

$$1 + 3 + 5 + \dots (2n-1) = n^2$$

5. Students are asked merely to verify the formula (i.e., see that it works). Using a calculator, they can experiment with several sets of values for T_n and test this formula. For example,

$$1 + 3 + 6 + 10 + 15 + 21 = \frac{(6)\,(7)\,(8)}{6} = 56$$

6. Similarly,

$$1 + 4 + 9 + 16 + 25 + 36 = \frac{(6)\,(7)\,(13)}{6} = 91$$

Name _____ Date _____

Piling Up Blocks

Ancient Babylonian and Egyptian mathematician–scribes were excellent record keepers. One of their tasks was to determine the quantities of bricks and building stones needed for the large structures built in their societies. Modern archaeologists have uncovered numerous lists and records of Babylonian and Egyptian building materials. One of the most impressive structures of the ancient Eastern world was the ziggurat, or step-pyramid. These "towers to heaven" were constructed from rectangular prisms stacked one upon another. Each prism was a pile of solid blocks. The ancients built their ziggurats by piling up blocks.

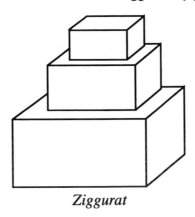

Ziggurat

These builders also knew how to compute the volume of a rectangular prism whose length was *b*, width was *w*, and height was *h*:

$$V = b \times h \times w$$

Using this basic formula as a reference, could the ancient scribes of Egypt and Babylonia have derived the formula for the volume of a rectangular pyramid? Let's pile up some blocks and find out.

Using large-square grid paper, where one grid square represents a block of building stone, sketch the indicated pyramids on the graph paper. Assume your building blocks are perfect cubes and that one unit of volume is one building block. Determine the number of blocks required to build each pyramid, and tabulate your results. Specifically, list height (*h*), base length (*b*), volume *V*, and volume of a corresponding solid prism *S* ($S = h \times b^2$). Also compute *V/S*.

1. A step pyramid of three levels. Each step has a width of two blocks. The prisms used have square bases and heights of 4, 3, and 3 blocks respectively, ascending from the bottom to the top. The bottom prism has a base of 10 blocks.

133   *Learning Activities from the History of Mathematics*

2. A step pyramid of five levels, with steps of one block width. All prisms have heights of 2 blocks. The base is 10 blocks wide.

3. A step pyramid of five levels. Each level is one block high. Steps are of one block width. Initial base is of 10 blocks.

4. For the last pyramid, the builders add one more block on the very top as a crown. Tabulate the resulting dimensions and resulting volumes.

5. For the pyramid constructed in step 3 above, the builders decide to fill in the steps and develop a pyramid with smooth sides.

   a. What is the volume of each one of the side blocks needed to smooth the side?

   b. What is the volume of a corner block?

   c. With the side and corner blocks added, what is the total volume of the pyramid?

   d. When we fill in *all* the steps, what happens to the dimensions of the base of the pyramid?

6. With these new building techniques perfected, the builders design a square-based pyramid with smooth sides that rise at a 45° angle and meet in a point or apex. The initial dimensions for the base and height of this pyramid are 11 and 6 blocks respectively. The completed pyramid will have different dimensions due to the addition of side, corner, and apex blocks.

   a. What is the volume for the required capstone or apex block for this pyramid?

   b. By counting blocks, determine the volume of this pyramid. What is it?

   c. How does this volume compare with that of the encompassing solid rectangular prism?

   What can you conclude from this series of exercises about the ability of ancient scribes to find a formula for the volume of a pyramid?

Piling Up Blocks—Teacher's Guide

Mathematical learning objective: processing of empirical data; mathematical deduction based on data

Materials needed: large-grid graph paper; ruler (optional) (*Note:* photocopy page 137 for student use.)

Notes and suggestions: This activity requires the students to construct simple models of a pyramid. Students record the number of blocks theoretically required to construct each pyramid (ziggurat). As the number of steps in each ziggurat increases, the resulting solid more closely resembles a square-based pyramid. As the volumes of these pyramids are computed, they should approach a limiting value $b^2(h/3)$.

1.

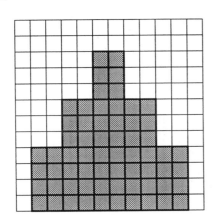

h	b	V	S	V/S
10	10	520	1,000	.52

2.

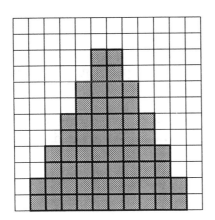

h	b	V	S	V/S
10	10	440	1,000	.440

3.

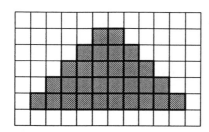

h	b	V	S	V/S
5	10	220	500	.44

4.

h	b	V	S	V/S
6	10	221	600	.368$\overline{3}$

5. a. $\frac{1}{2}$ unit^3

   b. $\frac{1}{3}$ unit^3

   c. $220 + 6\frac{2}{3}$ (corner blocks: $20 \times \frac{1}{3}$) + 60 (side blocks: $120 \times \frac{1}{2}$) = $286.\overline{66}$

   d. It increases in length by 2 blocks.

6. a. $\frac{1}{6}$ unit^3

   b. 286 units^3 (core blocks)
       72 units^3 (side blocks)
        8 units^3 (corner blocks)
       $\frac{1}{6}$ unit^3 (apex block)
       _____
       366.1$\overline{66}$ units^3

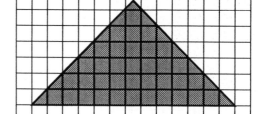

   c. The volume of the prism that could contain this pyramid is 1,098.5 units^3.

$$\frac{1,098.5}{366.1\overline{66}} = 3$$

   It is three times greater than the volume of the pyramid, or volume of pyramid = $(h/3)b^2$.

Conclusion: By careful record keeping and the actual counting of the blocks used, the builder of a pyramid could arrive at a formula for the volume of a pyramid.

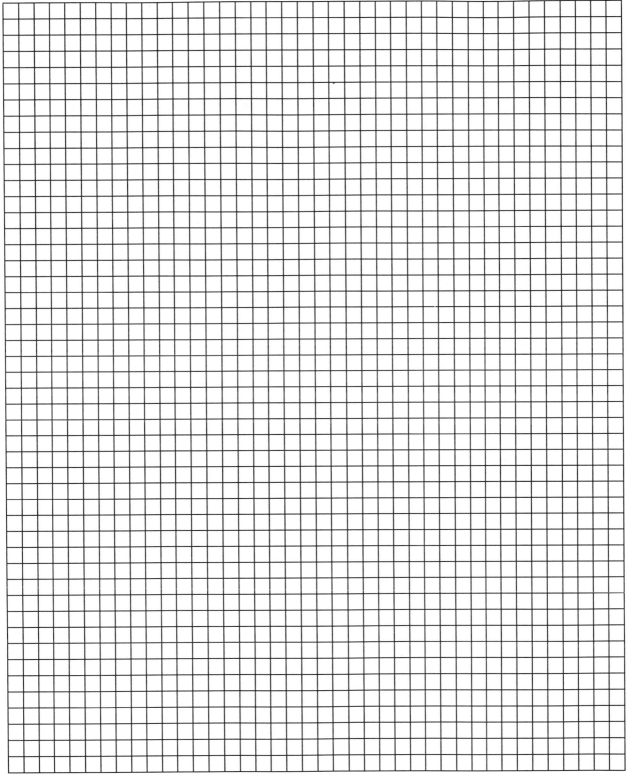

HLT 3

Building Up Volume

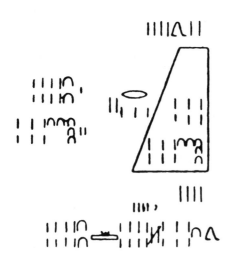

In ancient Egypt, written records were sometimes preserved on papyrus scrolls. Papyrus, an early form of paper made from water reeds, usually did not last long. However, a few such papyrus scrolls exist today, and they tell us much about life in ancient Egypt. Some of these scrolls are mathematical records or manuals. One such scroll was found in Egypt in 1893 and purchased for the Moscow Museum. It has become known as the Moscow papyrus. This scroll is about 18 feet long and 3 inches wide and is known to have been written in about 1890 B.C.—almost 4,000 years ago! Its contents consist of 25 problems involving the use of mathematics in daily life. The 14th problem on this list has been of special interest to math historians. The hieroglyphic form of this problem is given above. We find that the problem, when completely deciphered, illustrates how to find the volume for the frustum of a square pyramid when measures for the length of its sides, *a* and *b*, are given together with its height, *h*. See the illustration below. Does it look like anything shown in the papyrus inscription?

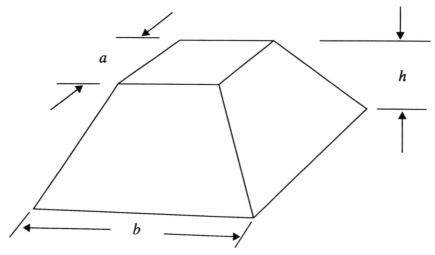

       Learning Activities from the History of Mathematics

It appears that the ancient Egyptians knew how to compute the volume for the frustum of a square pyramid. In this case:

$$V = \frac{h}{3}(a^2 + ab + b^2)$$

The question that has puzzled historians is how the Egyptians found the formula.

1. Let's explore one theory as to how the Egyptians might have discovered such a formula. Suppose a model of the frustum as shown was made out of clay. The model could be cut into different parts and the parts reassembled. If all the parts are used, the volume of the original frustum and the volume of the solid formed by the rearranged parts would be the same. Suppose the frustum is cut up or dissected into nine pieces as shown below:

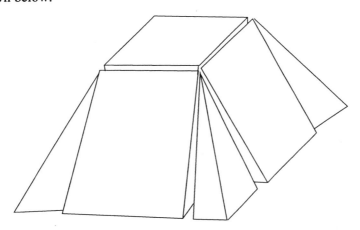

Assume that the measurements were as before, that is, the length of the upper base is a, the length of the lower base is b, and the height is h. On a clean sheet of paper make sketches of the three different solids resulting from the dissection. Label their sides accordingly.

Use these sketches to rearrange the pieces into shapes for which you can compute the volumes easily. Then combine the expressions for the volumes of the separate pieces. Can you obtain the Egyptian formula:

$$V = \frac{h}{3}(a^2 + ab + b^2)?$$

Most ancient societies developed formulas for the volume of geometric solids by dissecting the solids into a series of simpler solids whose volumes could easily be computed and then summing up the volumes of the individual pieces to obtain the volume of the whole. They knew that when working with the measure of volume that the whole was equal to the sum of its parts.

2. The ancient Chinese built burial chambers that were similar in shape to the frustum of a pyramid. Consider the diagram of such a chamber as shown below:

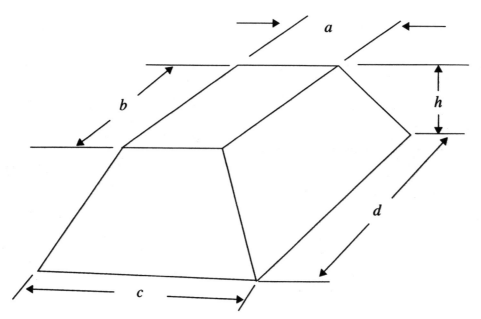

In the Chinese mathematical classic *The Nine Chapters on the Mathematical Arts* compiled in about 100 B.C., a formula for the volume of the burial chamber is given as:

$$V = \frac{1}{6}\left[(2a+c)b + (2c+a)d\right]h$$

It is believed that the Chinese used a method of dissection to arrive at this formula. On a clean sheet of paper, use sketches to dissect the burial chamber volume into simpler geometric solids. Compute the burial chamber volume by computing the volumes of the simpler solids and finding their sum. Is the Chinese formula correct?

3. The ancient Babylonians also had a formula for the volume of a truncated square pyramid:

$$V = h\left[\left(\frac{a+b}{2}\right)^2 + \frac{1}{3}\left(\frac{a-b}{2}\right)^2\right]$$

where *a*, *b*, and *h* correspond to the measurements given for the Egyptian formula. Show that this formula is equivalent to the one obtained by the Egyptians.

4. Why do you think all these ancient societies were concerned with the volume of the frustum of a pyramid?

Building Up Volume—Teacher's Guide

Mathematical learning objective: accomplish geometric proofs by use of dissection methods; strengthen skills of spatial perception

Materials needed: paper and pencil; clay (Plasticine) and wire/string (optional)

Notes and suggestions: The figure shown at the left of the hieroglyphic illustration ◿ represents the cross section of the volume to be computed. Some interesting hieroglyphics to be read are 🏛, representing $\frac{1}{3}$, and Λ, "walking legs" representing the operation of addition. The problem is to find the volume for the frustum of a square pyramid with sides of measure 2 and 4 and with height of 6 units. The answer is given as:

Combine this 16 with this 8 with this 4, and one obtains 28. Take $\frac{1}{3}$ of 6, giving 2; take 28 twice, giving 56. You see, it is 56, you have it correctly.

Students should sketch the solids, labeling all given dimensions, and graphically move them around until they realize simpler geometric shapes, that is, shapes whose volumes can easily be computed. This task can be worked with clay (Plasticine) models, with dissections made with a piece of taut wire or string; however, the work can get messy. Whether using sketches or clay models, this is a good small-group activity. Encourage discussion.

1.

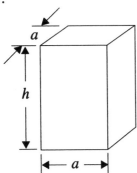

Central prism:

$$V = a^2h$$

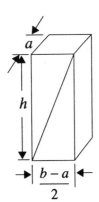

Side pieces; each pair forms a rectangular prism:

$$V = \left[\left(\frac{b-a}{2}\right)ah\right] \times 2 = abh - a^2h$$

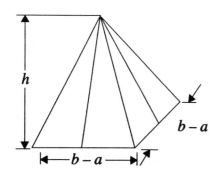

Corner pieces; four together form
a square pyramid:

$$V = (b-a)^2 \frac{h}{3} = (b^2 - 2ab + a^2)\frac{h}{3}$$

Adding all the pieces, we find:

$$(a^2 h) + (abh - a^2 h) + \frac{h}{3}(b^2 - 2ab + a^2)$$

$$= \frac{a^2 h}{3} + \frac{abh}{3} + \frac{b^2 h}{3} = \frac{h}{3}(a^2 + ab + b^2)$$

2.

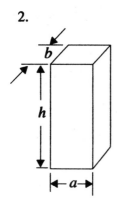

Central prism:

$$V = abh$$

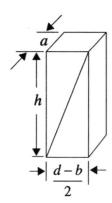

Side pieces; one set forms a
rectangular prism:

$$V = (a)\left(\frac{d-b}{2}\right)h = \frac{adh}{2} - \frac{abh}{2}$$

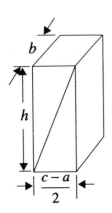

Side pieces; remaining set forms a rectangular prism:

$$V = (b)\left(\frac{c-a}{2}\right)h = \frac{cbh}{2} - \frac{abh}{2}$$

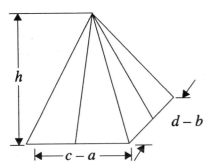

Corner pieces; four together form a rectangular pyramid:

$$\frac{h}{3}(c-a)(d-b) = \frac{hcd}{3} - \frac{adh}{3} - \frac{cbh}{3} + \frac{abh}{3}$$

Adding all the pieces together, we find:

$$V = \frac{adh}{6} + \frac{cbh}{6} + \frac{abh}{3} + \frac{cdh}{3} = \frac{1}{6}[(2a+c)b + (2c+a)d]$$

The Chinese formula is correct!

3. $$V = h\left[\left(\frac{a+b}{2}\right)^2 + \frac{1}{3}\left(\frac{a-b}{2}\right)^2\right]$$

$$= \left(\frac{a^2 + 2ab + b^2}{4}\right) + \left(\frac{a^2 - 2ab + b^2}{12}\right)$$

$$= \left(\frac{a^2}{4} + \frac{a^2}{12}\right) + \left(\frac{ab}{2} - \frac{ab}{6}\right) + \left(\frac{b^2}{4} + \frac{b^2}{12}\right)$$

$$= \frac{h}{3}(a^2 + ab + b^2)$$

4. If they used just unsupported stone to build a high structure such as a tower or wall, they were soon limited in the height they could achieve. However, if they inclined the side walls of the structure, a greater height could be reached. The resulting solid is the frustrum of a pyramid.

HLT 4

A Babylonian Discovery

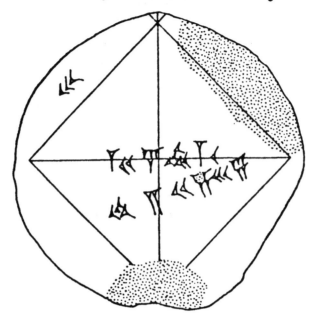

The illustration above is a facsimile of a Babylonian clay tablet inscribed in about 1600 B.C. It is presently in a collection of tablets owned by Yale University and is referred to as YBC (Yale Babylonian Collection) 7289. Mathematically speaking, the contents of this tablet are very interesting. Place yourself in the position of a mathematical archaeologist and let's see the discoveries you can make in examining this tablet.

1. Describe what you think the contents of the tablet concern.

2. The following facts are known about the Babylonian number system:

   a. It is a base 60 system.

   b. Two cuneiform symbols, ⟨ (10) and ▏ (1), are used in an additive manner to express all numbers.

   c. The system is positional and allows for sexagesimal fractions.

   Thus: ⟨⟨▏▏ / ⟨⟨▏ is translated in base 10 as 42 provided this grouping occupies the

   units position in the number.

   ⟨⟨▏▏▏⟨▏▏ is translated as $(22) \times 60^1 + 14 \times (60)^\circ = 1{,}334$.

⟨⟨|||⟨ 𝄂𝄂|| Adding a fractional expression to this number:

$$= 1,334 + \frac{2}{60}$$

With this knowledge you should be able to decipher the inscription on the tablet. What number do you think is written along the upper left edge of the square?

3. It has been determined that the inscription in the center of the square represents two distinct numbers. Consider the upper number; reading it from left to right, its positional groups are as indicated below, and it is known that the first position represents units:

What is this number in base 60? Convert it into a decimal number. Do you recognize this number? If so, what is it?

4. Using your conclusions from steps 2 and 3 above, what does the lower cuneiform number on the tablet represent in base 10?

Apparently, the ancient Babylonians could extract the square roots of numbers accurately to several sexagesimal places. How did they do it? Some historians believe they used an average-and-divide method as follows:

It is required to find $\sqrt{n}$:

a. Take a guess g_1 for the value $\sqrt{n}$

b. Then find $\dfrac{n}{g_1} = a_1$ and $\dfrac{a_1 + g_1}{2} = g_2$

c. Repeat this process: $\dfrac{n}{g_2} = a_2$, $\dfrac{a_2 + g_2}{2} = g_3$

until the desired accuracy is obtained for $\sqrt{n}$.

Suppose it is required to find $\sqrt{7}$:

   a. Let $g_1 = 2$.

   b. $\dfrac{7}{2} = 3.5, \dfrac{3.5 + 2}{2} = \dfrac{5.5}{2} = 2.75 = g_2$

   c. $\dfrac{7}{2.75} = 2.5454, \dfrac{2.75 + 2.5454}{2} = 2.647 = g_3$

   d. $\dfrac{7}{2.647} = 2.6445, \dfrac{2.647 + 2.645}{2} = 2.646$

Checking the value of $\sqrt{7}$ with a calculator, we obtain 2.6457513. Thus after three attempts we obtain accuracy to 3 decimal places.

5. Use this algorithm and a calculator to find:

     $\sqrt{12}$ $\sqrt{87}$

6. Other historians of mathematics feel that the Babylonians used another algorithm to obtain the square root of a given number:

$$\sqrt{a^2 + h} = a + h/2a$$

where a^2 is a known square close to the number whose square root is sought. Again assisted by a calculator, use this algorithm to find: $\sqrt{7}$, $\sqrt{12}$ and $\sqrt{87}$.

7. Which algorithm do you think is better? Explain your answer.

A Babylonian Discovery—Teacher's Guide

Mathematical learning objective: participate in an iterative mathematical approximation method; work with two algorithms for extracting square roots

Materials: hand calculator

Notes and suggestions: The divide-and-average algorithm for extracting square roots is an excellent example of an iterative process in mathematics. This task can be used as a learning experience within itself or in conjunction with work in computer science. Instructional material(s) on the Babylonian number system is very brief and is intended to serve simply as a review of the facts. Students undertaking this task should already have been exposed to the Babylonian number system and received drill in reading and writing Babylonian numerals.

1. Students should recognize the figure as that of a square with diagonals drawn.

2. $\langle\langle\langle$ = 30

3.
$$1 + \frac{24}{60} + \frac{51}{60^2} + \frac{10}{60^3} = 1 + \frac{2}{5} + \frac{51}{3{,}600} + \frac{1}{21{,}600}$$

$$= 1.4142129^{+} \approx \sqrt{2}$$

4.
$$42 + \frac{25}{60} + \frac{35}{60^2} = 30\sqrt{2}$$

5. Students should set up the algorithm but do the calculations with a calculator. Since different students may choose different initial guesses for $\sqrt{n}$ and the number of iterations may vary, results should be considered in a class discussion. Two possible answers are given below:

$\sqrt{12}$ Let $g_1 = 3$, then $\dfrac{12}{3} = 4$

$\dfrac{4 + 3}{2} = 3.5$, $g_2 = 3.5$ $\dfrac{12}{3.5} = 3.4286$

$\dfrac{3.4286 + 3.5}{2} = 3.4643$ $\sqrt{12} \approx 3.4643$

Calculator value $\sqrt{12} = 3.464101615$

$\sqrt{87}$ Let $g_1 = 9$, then $\dfrac{87}{9} = 9.\overline{66}$

$\dfrac{9.\overline{66} + 9}{2} = 9.\overline{33}$ $g_2 = 9.\overline{33}$ $\dfrac{87}{9.33} = 9.3214$

$$\frac{9.3333 + 9.3214}{2} = 9.32735 \quad g_3 = 9.32735$$

$$\sqrt{87} \approx 9.32735$$

Calculator value $\sqrt{87} = 9.32738$

6. $\sqrt{7} = \sqrt{4+3} \approx 2 + \dfrac{3}{4} = 2.75$

   $\sqrt{12} = \sqrt{9+3} \approx 3 + \dfrac{3}{6} = 3.5$

   $\sqrt{87} = \sqrt{81+6} \approx 9 + \dfrac{6}{18} = 9.\overline{33}$

7. What does "better" mean? The second algorithm is quicker. It gives a good approximate answer. However, the first algorithm allows the user to obtain as much accuracy as desired. If speed is required, the second algorithm is better. If accuracy is the important factor, then the first iterative-based algorithm is better.

HLT 5

Picking Up the Pieces

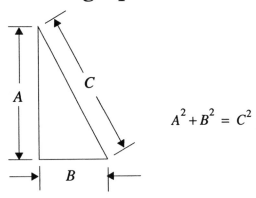

$$A^2 + B^2 = C^2$$

The above mathematical statement is usually called the Pythagorean theorem or Pythagorean proposition and was known and used by many ancient peoples long before Pythagoras received the credit for its conception. One of the oldest known proofs of this theorem is given in a Chinese diagram called the *hsuan-thu*.

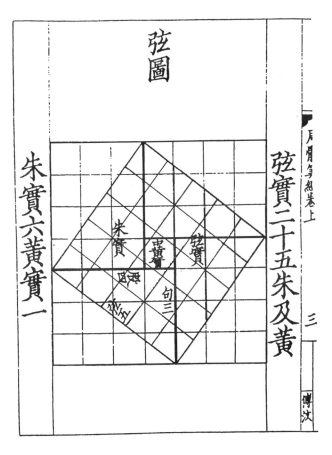

A copy of this diagram is shown at the left. Chinese mathematicians used an intuitive algebra based on geometric relationships. Thus they considered the product of two quantities $a \times b$ as a geometric area of a rectangle with width a and length b. Consider the relationships evident in the *hsuan-thu*. The inner figure consists of four congruent right triangles and one small square. Let the sides of the triangles be labeled A, B, C as shown above. Then:

1. What is the area of the large central figure in the *hsuan-thu*?

2. Carefully cut the *hsuan-thu* diagram at the end of this unit into its component geometric shapes: one small square and eight triangles. Rearrange these pieces to prove that $A^2 + B^2 = C^2$.

3. Develop the same proof using algebraic statements.

4. Consider the area of the whole large square. How can you express this algebraically using the designations for A, B, and C as stated?

5. Use this last algebraic statement and the geometric relations present within the *hsuan-thu* to arrive at the expression $A^2 + B^2 = C^2$.

6. Is this method of picking up the pieces and rearranging them a proof? Explain your answer.

The ancient Chinese had many interesting problems involving right triangles. Consider the problem of a circle inscribed in a right triangle as illustrated below.

7. Let the sides of the right triangle be labeled, as before A, B, C. Use the copy of the illustration given at the end of this unit and your knowledge of Chinese geometric algebra to show that the radius R of the given circle is expressed by:

$$R = \frac{A \times B}{A + B + C}$$

圓 圓 容 股 句

Cut up the figure and pick up the pieces. (*Hint:* Use the whole given area as shown. Duplicate the geometric situation above the diagonal so that you will have two circles and sets of triangles to work with.)

句 股 容 圓 圓

Note: This is an old Chinese diagram drawn with a brush. Geometrically it is incorrect—the circle should be tangent to the long leg and hypotenuse of the right triangle. Assume it is in working the solution.

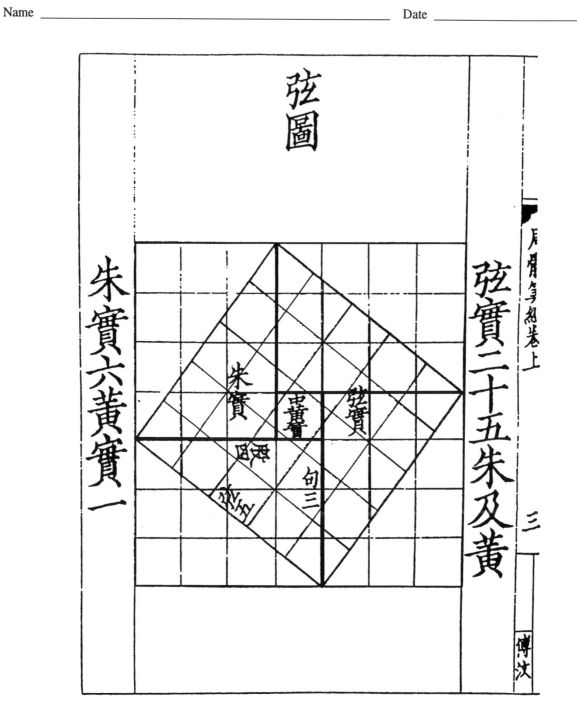

The Hsuan-Thu

Picking Up the Pieces—Teacher's Guide

Mathematical learning objective: perform a geometric-based proof of the Pythagorean theorem; realize that mathematical proofs and theorems are not necessarily named after the person who discovered them

Materials needed: scissors

Notes and suggestions: The earliest work in algebra in Babylonia, Greece, and China depended on the use of geometric intuition. Early peoples visualized algebraic relationships aided by drawings and diagrams. Students find experiences with geometric-based algebra very satisfying.

1. The area of the large central square is C^2.

2.

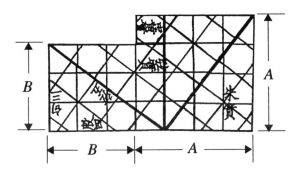

$$A^2 + B^2 = C^2$$

3. Area of four triangles, $4\dfrac{(AB)}{2}$; area of small square, $(A - B)^2$; $C^2 = (A - B)^2 + 4\dfrac{(AB)}{2}$

   $= A^2 + B^2$

4. The area of the large square is $(A + B)^2$.

5. It can be seen that the area of the large square $(A + B)^2$ is equal to the sum of the areas of the four outside triangles and the central large square, C^2. Thus,

$$(A + B)^2 = 4\frac{(AB)}{2} + C^2$$

$$A^2 + 2AB + B^2 = 2AB + C^2 \qquad \text{or}$$

$$A^2 + B^2 = C^2$$

6. Yes, it is a proof, because it concretely shows that the algebraic relationships are true. Since *A*, *B*, and *C* can vary, the relationships that are discovered are general in nature.

7. The pieces should be cut out and rearranged as follows:

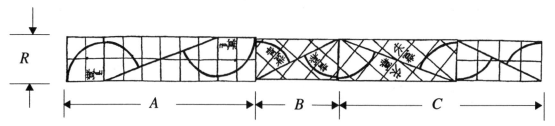

Name _____   Date _____

Algebra with Lines

ΑΓΕΩΜΕΤΡΗΤΟΣ
ΜΗΔΕΙΣ ΕΙΣΙΤΩ

Plato

The above motto was said to be written over the entrance to Plato's Academy. For the Greeks, geometry was the highest form of mathematics. It was orderly and beautiful, a worthy subject upon which to reason. Thus it was natural that when the Greeks reached out into other areas of mathematics, their reasoning would be tied to geometric experiences. Indeed, the Greeks were the first people to conceive of a mathematical magnitude being represented by the length of a line segment. They manipulated such line segments to develop algebraic theories.

The classical tools of Greek geometry were the straightedge, used for drawing line segments, and the compass, used for drawing circles and arcs but not permitted as an instrument for transferring distances. Thus algebra could be done with the straightedge and the compass.

Let's duplicate some Greek algebraic results. Using just a straightedge and a compass, perform some geometric constructions to find the magnitudes required.

Given: the following line segments:

_____   magnitude 1 unit
_____   magnitude *b* units
_____   magnitude *c* units

Transfer these line segments onto a blank sheet of paper. (*Note:* For this transfer you may use a compass, but once the line segment is drawn, you may not use the compass to measure off that distance again.)

Perform Euclidean constructions to find:

1. $a + b$

2. $a - b$

3. $a \times b$

4. a / b

5. $\sqrt{a}$

6. $\sqrt{ab}$

         Learning Activities from the History of Mathematics

Algebra with Lines—Teacher's Guide

Mathematical learning objective: undertake a problem-solving experience and obtain practice in performing Euclidean constructions

Materials needed: drawing compass; ruler; blank, unlined paper

Notes and suggestions: Students may trace the line segments onto the working paper or use their compass to lay out the lengths. The first two exercises are straightforward and rather obvious. If students get stuck on the latter exercises, they may require a hint. Ask them to think about similar triangles or find proportions that will satisfy the required statement and then devise constructions to fulfill the proportions.

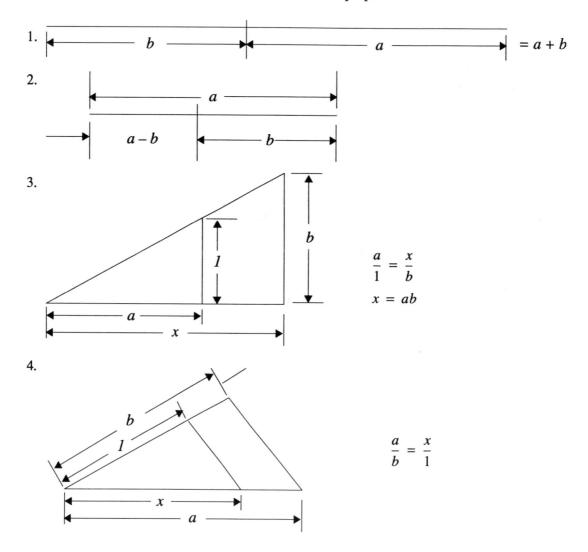

5.

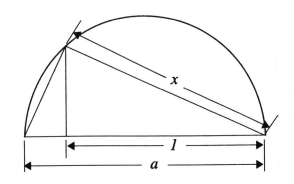

$$\frac{a}{x} = \frac{x}{1}$$

$$x^2 = a, \; x = \sqrt{a}$$

6.

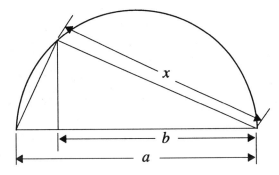

$$\frac{a}{x} = \frac{x}{b}$$

$$x^2 = ab, \; x = \sqrt{ab}$$

HLT 7

The Platonic Solids

CUBE
Earth

TETRAHEDRON
Fire

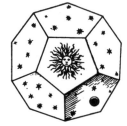

OCTAHEDRON
Air

DODECAHEDRON
the Universe

ICOSAHEDRON
Water

The ancient Greeks were fascinated by regularities that are found in mathematics. For example, they realized that only certain regular polygons were easily constructible using only a straightedge and a compass. Which polygons are these? The Pythagoreans extended this search for regularities into three dimensions by seeking out regular polyhedra, that is, polyhedra whose faces are composed of congruent, regular polygons. They found that there were only five such polyhedra: the tetrahedron, the cube, the octahedron, the icosahedron and the dodecahedron. Soon mystical properties were assigned to these polyhedra. By the time of Plato's Academy (ca. 360 B.C.), the tetrahedron became associated with fire; the cube was associated with the earth; the octahedron represented air; the icosahedron, water; and the dodecahedron represented the universe. This collection of solids became known as the Platonic solids.

1. On the following pages are grids for each of the Platonic solids. Cut out these grids, fold them along the indicated edges, and tape the edges together to form the solids. Examine each solid carefully. Identify the faces, the vertices, and the edges of each solid. How many faces does each solid have?

2. Explain why there are only five such solids.

3. The members of Plato's Academy believed that all matter was composed of these solids. If stacked up like blocks, which solids could fill space?

4. An interesting formula relates the number of vertices (*V*), the number of faces (*F*), and the number of edges (*E*) for the Platonic solids. This formula seems to have been first

Name _____ Date _____

stated by the French mathematician René Descartes (1596–1650) in about 1635. In 1752, it was again discovered by Leonhard Euler (1707–1783) and has since been called Euler's formula. Fill in the chart below and attempt to find Euler's formula.

	V	F	E
Tetrahedron			
Cube			
Octahedron			
Dodecahedron			
Icosahedron			

5. Sketch several different polyhedra. Does Euler's formula work for them?

6. Visualize the centers of the faces of a cube connected by straight lines. These lines will form a regular polygon. Which polygon is it? This polygon is said to be the dual of the cube. Which polygon is its own dual?

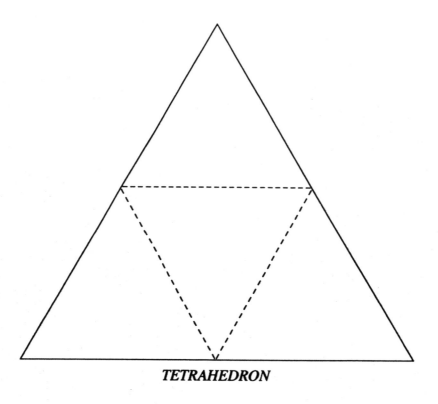

TETRAHEDRON

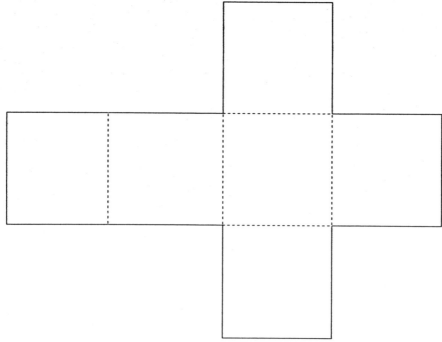

CUBE

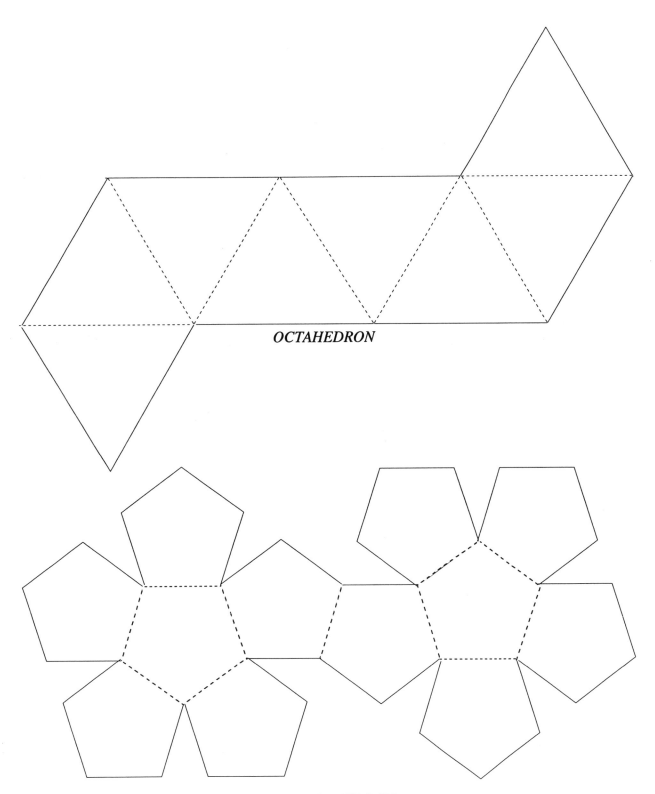

OCTAHEDRON

DODECAHEDRON

Learning Activities from the History of Mathematics

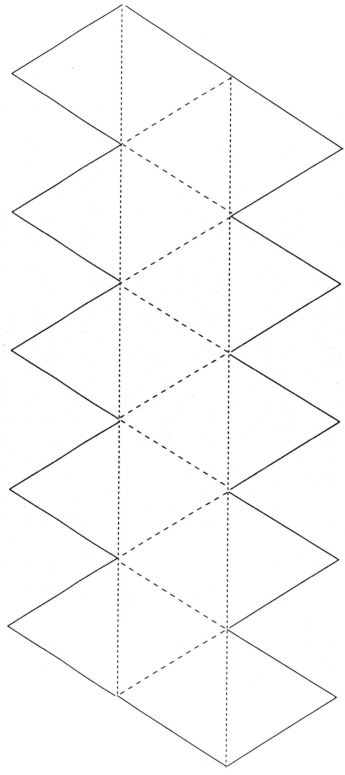

ICOSAHEDRON

Learning Activities from the History of Mathematics

The Platonic Solids—Teacher's Guide

Mathematical learning objective: provide practice in pattern recognition; introduce students to topological properties of solids

Materials needed: scissors; cellophane tape; or alternately, polydron pieces may be purchased

Notes and suggestions: Encourage students to experiment with their polyhedra. A classroom discussion could focus on "Where have you seen such solids?" Perhaps some students could build a bigger set out of cardboard. Platonic solids can be suspended by string to form an interesting mobile.

1. tetrahedron, 4 faces; cube, 6 faces; octahedron, 8 faces; dodecahedron, 12 faces; icosahedron, 20 faces

2. Recall how the polyhedra were folded during construction. If any corner (vertex) is flattened, the sum of the angles of the polygons joined at that point will be less than 360°. (If not, it couldn't be folded.) Systematically consider the possibilities for joining regular polygons. Of course there must be at last three faces at each vertex to make a solid. Consider how each regular polygon could possibly be used to form a polyhedra.

   equilateral triangle: 3 together form an angle of 180°, gives tetrahedron

   equilateral triangle: 4 together form an angle of 240°, gives octahedron

   equilateral triangle: 5 together form an angle of 300°, gives icosahedron

   square   : 3 together form an angle of 270°, gives cube

   pentagon   : 3 together form an angle of 324°, gives dodecahedron

   None others possible

3. Cubes

4.

V	F	E
4	4	6
8	6	12
6	8	12
20	12	30
12	20	30

$V + F - E = 2$

5.

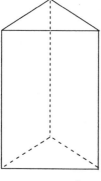

$6 + 5 - 9 = 2$

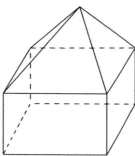

$9 + 9 - 16 = 2$
etc.

Since the students will devise a variety of polyhedra, have several students draw and discuss their results at the chalkboard.

6.

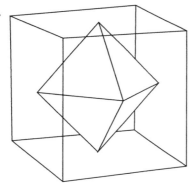

An octahedron.
The dual of a tetrahedron is a tetrahedron.

HLT 8

The Golden Mean

One of the most famous buildings of antiquity is the Parthenon, found on the Acropolis in Athens, Greece. This majestic temple built between 447 and 432 B.C. was dedicated to the goddess of wisdom, Athena. Since that time, this building has been admired for its stately beauty and pleasing shape. The Greeks built this temple to reflect harmony, and to them harmony was expressed through mathematical ratios. Mathematical ratio is a special feature in the design of the Parthenon. Let's find that ratio.

It has been said that Pythagoras in his travels through Mesopotamia learned of three mathematical means that could be found involving two numbers, a and b, where $a < b$:

1. the arithmetic mean, $A = \dfrac{a+b}{2}$

2. the geometric mean, $G = \sqrt{ab}$

3. the harmonic mean, $H = \dfrac{2ab}{a+b}$

Using these means, the Pythagoreans found another mean called the golden mean. This mean, or variations of it, have been associated with various natural phenomena such as the growth of trees or flowers. It also possesses special aesthetic appeal and frequently is incorporated into works of art and architecture. Let's examine this mean more closely.

Given a line segment $\overline{AB}$ choose a point C on this line so that

$$\left|\frac{AB}{AC}\right| = \left|\frac{AC}{CB}\right|$$

●————————————————————————————●————————●
A C B

$\dfrac{AB}{AC}$ Under these circumstances, point C is said to have divided AB into a golden section, and is called the golden ratio.

1. Let $|AB| = 1$, $|AC| = x$; find a numerical value for the golden ratio.

2. A rectangle the lengths of whose sides are in the golden ratio is called a golden rectangle. On a blank piece of paper, using a straightedge (no measurement allowed) and a compass, construct a golden rectangle as follows:

   a. Construct a square ☐ $ABCD$.

   b. Construct the midpoint M of $\overline{CD}$.

   c. Construct point E on $\overleftrightarrow{DC}$ so that $\overline{MB} \cong \overline{ME}$.

   d. Construct the point F of the perpendicular from E to $\overleftrightarrow{AB}$.

   e. The ☐ $AFED$ is a golden rectangle.

3. Use algebra to prove $\left|\dfrac{AF}{FE}\right|$ is the golden ratio.

4. Show that ☐ $BFEC$ is also a golden rectangle. Can you construct another golden rectangle in ☐ $BFEC$?

5. On the following page is a scale drawing of the Parthenon. Construct a rectangle containing the Parthenon. Is it a golden rectangle?

6. Standard index cards are usually in two sizes: $3'' \times 5''$ and $5'' \times 8''$. Are they golden rectangles? Measure the small end of a building brick and the face dimensions of an average paperback book. Determine the ratio of some cooperative classmates' total height to their navel height. What do you find?

7. The Pythagoreans used a secret sign for identification known as a pentagram. Given a regular pentagon, if all possible diagonals are drawn within the pentagon, a regular pentagonal star is formed. The pentagon and its star is called a pentagram. A pentagram has many unusual properties, one of which is that it generates another pentagon in which another pentagonal star can be formed, so the pentagram regenerates itself. The pentagram also contains many golden ratios. Find $\left|\dfrac{AD}{ED}\right|$ on the pentagram on the following page. Can you discover other golden ratios in this pentagram? There are many.

8. What is a golden triangle?

Parthenon

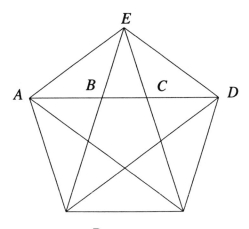

Pentagram

The Golden Mean—Teacher's Guide

Mathematical learning objective: to obtain a knowledge of the golden ratio

Materials needed: ruler; drawing compass; paper

Notes and suggestions: This activity opens the door to a variety of exercises involving the golden ratio and Fibonacci numbers. Many of these exercises can bring considerations of art, nature, and architecture into mathematics lessons. If you are interested in pursuing such an approach, seek out resources on the golden proportion. Several are listed in the bibliography at the end of this book.

1. If $|AB| = 1$, $|AC| = x$, and $\left|\dfrac{AB}{AC}\right| = \left|\dfrac{AC}{CB}\right|$ then:

$$\frac{1}{x} = \frac{x}{1-x} \Rightarrow x^2 + x - 1 = 0 \text{ and } x = \frac{-1 \pm \sqrt{5}}{2}$$

Selecting the positive value, $x = .618$ and the golden ratio is $\dfrac{1}{.618} = 1.618$

2.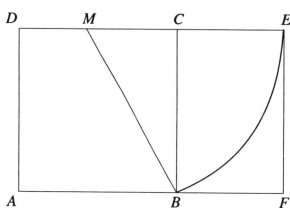

3. Let $AB = x$, then $ME = \dfrac{x\sqrt{5}}{2}$ and $AF = \dfrac{x(1 + \sqrt{5})}{2}$.

   Since $FE = x$, $\dfrac{AF}{FE} = \dfrac{1 + \sqrt{5}}{2} = 1.618$.

4. In $\boxed{}BFEC$, $FE = x$, $BF = \dfrac{x\sqrt{5}}{2} - \dfrac{x}{2} = \dfrac{x(\sqrt{5} - 1)}{2}$.

   Then:
   $$\frac{EF}{BF} = \frac{\left(\dfrac{1}{\sqrt{5} - 1}\right)}{2} = 1.618$$

Yes. Construct a square of side *CE* in ☐ *BFEC*. With a compass centered at point *E*, scribe an arc with radii *CE*; where this arc intersects $\overline{EF}$ is point *K*. Through *K* construct $\overline{KP} \parallel CE$; point *P* is on $\overline{CB}$. The remaining region of ☐ *BFEC*, *BFKP*, is a golden rectangle. The golden rectangle is self-generating. Given any golden rectangle, you can always construct another golden rectangle within it.

5. Students may circumscribe the Parthenon with a rectangle directly or else lay a blank piece of paper on top of the illustration and draw the required rectangle on that construction paper. Results will vary. My rectangle of $4\frac{7}{8} \times 3$ gives a result of 1.625.

6. The cards are $\frac{5}{3} = 1.\overline{66}$ and $\frac{8}{5} = 1.6$. These values are close to the golden ratio while complying with manufacturing standards—would it be wise to manufacture paper with fractional dimensions? Answers may vary slightly. My brick gives a ratio of 1.764; the cover of a paperback book, 1.465. Both values are close to the golden proportion. Total height to navel height for a human should approximate the golden ratio. The artist Leonardo da Vinci discovered this fact and found the golden ratio within several sets of measurements concerning the human body.

7. Circumscribing the pentagram with a circle will help in determining the measure of the various angles within the pentagram.

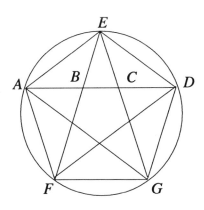

An interior angle of the pentagram is 108°. The diagonals drawn to any interior angle of the pentagram trisect it.

In $\triangle ADE$, $\angle EAD = \angle EDA = 36°$ and $\angle AED = 108°$.

In $\triangle ECD$, $\angle CED = \angle EDC = 36°$ and $\angle ECD = 108°$. $\triangle ADE \sim \triangle ECD$,

then $\dfrac{AD}{ED} = \dfrac{ED}{CD}$.

Let $AD = 1$, $(ED)^2 = CD$, but $CD = AB$ and $AB = 1 - ED$.

Therefore, $(ED)^2 = 1 - ED$. Solving for *ED*, we find $ED = .61803$ and $\left|\dfrac{AD}{ED}\right| = 1.61803$, the golden ratio. $\left|\dfrac{AD}{CD}\right|$, $\dfrac{AC}{CD}$ and $\dfrac{AD}{AE}$ also gives the golden ratio.

8. An isosceles triangle is called a golden triangle if the ratio of one of its sides to its base is $\dfrac{1 + \sqrt{5}}{2} = 1.618$.

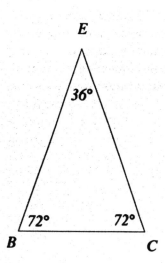

Triangles *BEC* and *FEG* from the pentagram on the preceding page are golden triangles. How many other golden triangles can you and your students find in the pentagram?

HLT 9

The Bridge of Fools

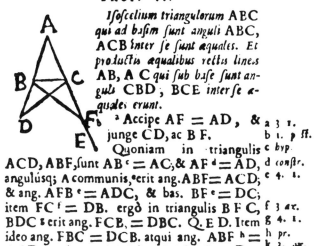

PROP. V.

Isoscelium triangulorum ABC qui ad basim sunt anguli ABC, ACB inter se sunt aquales. Et productis aqualibus rettis lineis AB, A C qui sub base sunt anguli CBD; BCE inter se aquales erunt.

ª Accipe AF = AD, & junge CD, ac B F.

Quoniam in triangulis ACD, ABF, sunt AB ᶜ = AC, & AF ᵈ = AD, angulúsq; A communis, erit ang. ABF = ACD; & ang. AFB ᵉ = ADC, & bas. BF ᵉ = DC; item FC ᶠ = DB. ergò in triangulis B F C, BDC ᵍ erit ang. FCB, = DBC. Q. E D. Item ideo ang. FBC = DCB. atqui ang. ABF ʰ = ACD. ergò ang. ABC ᵏ = ACB. Q. E. D.

a 3 1.
b 1. p st.
c byp.
d constr.
e 4. 1.
f 3 ar.
g 4. 1.
h pr.
k 3. ax.

Corollarium.

Hinc, Onne triangulum æquilaterum est queq; æquiangulum.

PROP.

Historically, the first individual credited with specific mathematical discoveries was the Greek Thales of Miletus (ca. 640–546 B.C.). As a merchant, Thales traveled widely and learned the mathematical skills of the peoples with whom he traded, particularly the Egyptians and the Babylonians. History credits Thales with six specific geometric propositions, among which is the fact that the base angles of an isosceles triangle are congruent. This proposition was formalized by Euclid in his *Elements* and included as a theorem (Book I, Theorem V).

Throughout the Middle Ages, in European society the proof of this particular theorem became the test of a person's geometric knowledge. If you could accomplish the proof, you knew geometry, if not, you were a "fool." Euclid's version of the theorem, which was duplicated, became known in Latin as *pons asinorum*, "the bridge of asses" or "bridge of fools." Only a few could cross this bridge. The diagram above is from a 17th-century text. Although you may not be able to read the Latin, you should be able to follow the proof.

1. Use this Latin version to reconstruct "the bridge of fools" proof. (*Some help:* Given isosceles triangle *ABC*, prove that angle *ACB* equals angle *ABC*. Sides *AB* and *AC* are extended so that *AD* = *AF* [apparently points *E* and *F* coincide]. It is also accepted that *AB* = *AC*.)

2. Construct your own proof to show that the base angles of an isosceles triangle are congruent.

3. **Library research:** Pappus of Alexandria (ca. A.D. 300) constructed a very elegant proof for this theorem. Find Pappus' proof and compare it with the one given by Euclid. Which proof is better? Why?

The Bridge of Fools—Teacher's Guide

Mathematical learning objective: practice in constructing geometric proofs; realization
   that there are sometimes several ways to obtain a proof of the same geometric principle

Materials needed: paper; pencil; ruler

Notes and suggestions: This activity allows students to see several different proofs for a
   very basic geometric proposition. The classical proof is rather complex. Why is this so?
   Could a proof be made difficult in order to prevent people from learning it, thereby
   preserving geometric knowledge for a selected few individuals? Pappus' proof utilizes
   the concept of a geometric transformation and was very advanced and unusual for its
   time.

1.

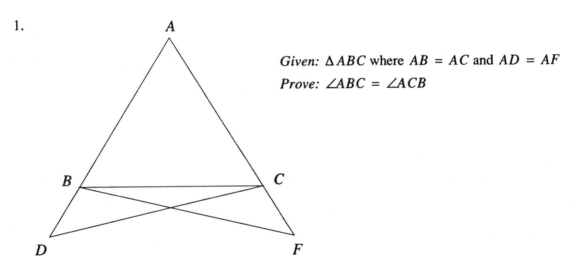

Given: $\triangle ABC$ where $AB = AC$ and $AD = AF$

Prove: $\angle ABC = \angle ACB$

In $\triangle ACD$ and $\triangle ABF$, $AB = AC$ (given), $AD = AF$ (by construction),
$\angle BAF \cong \angle CAD$ (reflexive property of $\cong$). Therefore $\triangle ACD \cong \triangle ABF$ (SAS). Then in
$\triangle ACD$ and $\triangle ABF$, $BF = CD$ (corresponding parts). In $\triangle BFC$ and $\triangle CDB$,
$BD = CF$ (given), $BF = CD$ (above), and $BC = BC$ (reflexive property).

Therefore $\triangle BFC \cong \triangle CDB$ (SSS). From these sets of congruent triangles, we know
$\angle ABF = \angle ACD$ and $\angle CBF = \angle BCD$. Therefore $\angle ABF - \angle CBF =$
$\angle ACD - \angle BCD$, or $\angle ABC = \angle ACB$.

2.

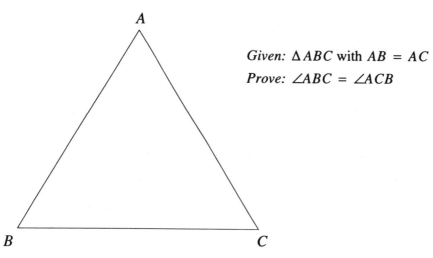

Given: △*ABC* where *AB* = *AC*

Prove: ∠*ABC* = ∠*ACB*

In △*ABC*, construct bisector of ∠*A* intersecting $\overline{BC}$ at point *M*. Now in △*BAM* and △*CAM*, *AB* = *AC* (given), ∠*BAM* = ∠*CAM* (definition of bisector), and *AM* = *AM* (reflexive property). Therefore, △*BAM* ≅ △*CAM* (SAS) and ∠*ABC* = ∠*ACB* (corresponding parts) QED.

3. Pappus' proof: He views the triangle as two triangles: one read from the left, the other, from the right.

Given: △*ABC* with *AB* = *AC*

Prove: ∠*ABC* = ∠*ACB*

In △*ABC* and △*ACB*, *AB* = *AC* (given), *AC* = *AB* (given), and ∠*BAC* = ∠*CAB*. Therefore △*ABC* ≅ △*ACB* (SAS) and ∠*ABC* = ∠*ACB* (corresponding parts) QED.

In his visualization of the situation, Pappus rotated △*BAC* about its line of symmetry: *AB* maps onto *AC*, *AC* maps onto *AB*, ∠*BAC* is fixed; ∠*ABC* maps onto ∠*ACB*. This is basically a proof in transformation geometry.

HLT 10

Decimal Mysteries

SECONDE PARTIE DE LA DISME DE L'OPE-RATION.

PROPOSITION I, DE L'ADDITION.

Estant donnez nombres de Disme à ajouster : Trouver leur somme :

Explication du donné. Il y a trois ordres de nombres de Disme, desquels le premier 27 ⓪8①4②7③, le deuxiesme 37 ⓪8①7②5③, le troisiesme 875 ⓪7①8②2③.

Explication du requis. Il nous faut trouver leur somme. *Construction.* On mettra les nombres donnez en ordre comme ci joignant, les aioustant selon la vulgaire maniere d'aiouster nombres entiers; en ceste sorte :

$$
\begin{array}{ccccc}
⓪ & ① & ② & ③ \\
2 & 7 & 8 & 4 & 7 \\
3 & 7 & 6 & 7 & 5 \\
8 & 7 & 5 & 7 & 8 & 2 \\
\hline
9 & 4 & 1 & 3 & 0 & 4 \\
\end{array}
$$

Donne somme (par le 1 probleme de l'Arithmetique) 941304, qui sont (ce que demonstrent les signes dessus les nombres) 941 ⓪3①0②4③. Ie di, que les mesmes sont la somme requise. *Demonstration.* Les 27 ⓪8①4②7③ donnez, font (par la 3e definition) $27\frac{8}{10}$, $\frac{4}{100}$, $\frac{7}{1000}$, ensemble $27\frac{847}{1000}$, & par mesme raison les 37 ⓪6①7②5③ vallent $37\frac{675}{1000}$, & les 8.75 ⓪7①8②4③ feront $875\frac{782}{1000}$, lesquels trois nombres, comme $27\frac{847}{1000}$, $37\frac{675}{1000}$, $875\frac{782}{1000}$, font ensemble (par le 10e probleme de l'Arith.) $941\frac{304}{1000}$, mais autant vaut aussi la somme 941 ⓪3①0②4③, c'est

Simon Stevin (1548–1620), a Flemish engineer, is the man usually credited with the invention of the theory of decimal fractions. In 1585, Stevin published a work called *La Disme*, which in French means *The Tenth*. In this book he explained his new method of writing fractions. A page of this work is shown above. Even though you may not be able to read

French, you can understand Stevin's mathematics. He designates decimal places by using the symbols ⓪ ① ② . . . , which in turn denote the zero decimal place (the decimal point), the first decimal place, the second decimal place, and so on.

1. Examine the page from *La Disme*. Do you understand Stevin's technique? If so, rewrite the following expressions using Stevin's form:

    87.93

    $\dfrac{68}{1,000}$

    321

    2.05481

    Why do you think this technique has gone out of fashion? Why don't we use it today?

2. In the *Treviso Arithmetic* written in 1478 anonymously, the author performs several division operations in which he or she divides a given number by 100. In each instance, the author marked off the last two digits of the number by the symbol ∟. For example, in considering a payment problem where it is required to find 18,248 ÷ 100, the answer is given as 182∟48.

    Is this author using a system of decimal fractions?

3. In 1492 the Italian Francesco Pellos wrote an arithmetic book in which many people think he used a decimal point. Often a page from the Pellos arithmetic book is shown as an example of this early decimal point in action. Here is the page.

Partir per means "partition by" or "divide by."

Examine the calculations shown on this page. Do you think Pellos understood decimal fractions? Justify your answer with specific examples.

The noted historian of mathematics David E. Smith considers the German mathematician Christoff Rudolff (ca. 1525) to be the first European to understand fully the concept and use of decimal fractions. Smith cites evidence from Rudolff's 1530 book *Exempel-büchlin*, in which the author computed a table of compound interest, shown on the following page. While perhaps you cannot read the German, you should be able to figure out the mathematical computations taking place.

375.   1875.
fl. 393|75 hauptgůt vn̄ gewin des erst jars.
 196875
  413|4375 Andern
   206718 75
   434|109375 Dritten
    21705 46875
   455|814843 75 Vierdten
    227907421875
   478|6055859375 Fünfften
    2393027929 6875
   502|535865234375 Sechsten
     25126793261718 75
    527|6626584960 9375 Sibenden
     26383132924804 6875
   554|045791420808 4375 Achtten
    27702289571044921875
   581|74808099194335 9375 Neundten
    29087404090597 167968 75
fl.610|835485041540527343 75 Zehēd
 ß 6|6878803323242 18 75000
 S 20|61640996972656250000.

72 Die 120 fl. tragē 2 jar p hauptgůt zins vnd
zinszins 132 fl. 2 ß 12 S. Bringt zinß vn̄ zinszins
12 fl. 2 ß 12 S. Darnach die 250 fl. tragē 3 jar
Baupeg. zins vn̄ zinszinß 289 fl. 3 ß 7 S. Vnd
ist halber zins des vierdtē jars 7 fl. 1 ß 26. S. 15

4. Smith claims the vertical bar as exhibited in some numbers is a decimal point. Is he correct?

5. Is Rudolff consistent in his use of symbolism?

6. If this is a compound interest problem, what is the rate of interest compounded each time?

7. Would you agree with Smith that Rudolff understood the use of decimal fractions?

8. After having examined all this historical evidence, who do you think invented decimals?

Should Simon Stevin receive the credit for this mathematical advance?

Decimal Mysteries—Teacher's Guide

Mathematical learning objective: practice recognizing decimal fractions

Materials needed: pencil and paper; calculator

Notes and suggestions: This activity should impress the students with the fact that mathematical concepts and techniques often have a long history of development and that many people participate in that development.

1. $87.93 \qquad = 8 \ 7 \ ⓪ \ 9 \ ① \ 3 \ ②$

    $321\dfrac{68}{1,000} = 3 \ 2 \ 1 \ ⓪ \ 0 \ ① \ 6 \ ② \ 8 \ ③$

    $2.05481 \quad = 2 \ ⓪ \ 0 \ ① \ 5 \ ② \ 4 \ ③ \ 8 \ ④ \ 1 \ ⑤$

    Stevin's technique went out of fashion because it uses a great amount of space. Once the ⓪ place is established, the user can visually count the places to its right.

2. The *Treviso* author shows that he or she knows how to divide by 100 (move the decimal place 2 units to the left) but demonstrates no other decimal knowledge or skills. No, he or she is not using a system of decimal fractions.

3. Although Pellos seems to use a decimal point—for example, 79654839.7 ÷ 20—he writes his result as $39827419\dfrac{17}{20}$ instead of expressing $\dfrac{17}{20}$ as .85. He does not carry the decimal point into his answer and does not seem to understand decimal fractions.

4. Rudolff's table provides the following data:
    375 *fl* were invested in a compound interest situation
    393.75 is the result of the first compounding
    413.4375 is the result of the second compounding
    434.109375 is the result of the third compounding
    and so on.

    Using a calculator and the compounding interest formula, find *r*:
    $$393.75 = 375(1+r)^1, \ r = .05$$
    Testing this value with some other given results, we see that it works. For example:
    $$375(1.05)^4 = 455.8148438$$
    The vertical bar is in fact a decimal point.

5. Rudolff is consistent with his use of symbolism.

6. His rate of interest is 5%.

7. Yes, he understands decimal fractions.

8. This experience should result in an answer that no one invented decimal fractions—many people contributed to their adoption and use.

    Stevin receives the credit because he was the first to publish a comprehensive theory of decimal fractions.

Medieval Multiplication

Since earliest times, mathematicians have sought easier ways to perform numerical computations. Special rules were devised for calculating with the aid of such devices as sticks, pebbles, sand tables, and the abacus. Usually such rules were very complex, especially those concerning multiplication and division.

In medieval Europe the possession of a computing device such as an abacus and knowledge of the rules necessary to use it were limited to a few people, called masters of the abacus or reckoning masters. Many of these men were also merchants, and it is from this group that the concept of a professional mathematician arose. The livelihood of a reckoning master was very good, so these masters jealously guarded their special knowledge, sharing it only with a few selected apprentices. These apprentices paid handsomely to learn the skills and arts of a mathematician.

Gradually from the 13th century onward, a new set of symbols, the Hindu-Arabic numerals, were used to represent numbers. They replaced the awkward Roman numerals that had been used for over a thousand years to record mathematical transactions. The new numerals also brought with them new techniques of computing that only required the use of a pen and paper. Now almost everyone could learn how to perform numerical calculations. Let's examine one of the new ways people in the 15th century learned to do multiplication.

First they learned their basic multiplication facts. Printed Pythagorean tables such as the following helped them in this task.

1. Have you seen a table of numbers like this before?

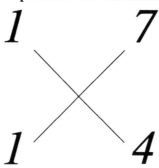

How was the table used?

Why is there a diagonal line on this table?

After students knew their multiplication facts, they could progress to the task of multiplying two 2-digit numbers. The method they used was called *per croxetta* in Italian. This meant "by the cross." Consider finding the product of 17 and 14:

a. First multiply 4 by 7; the product is 28. Write down the 8 and retain the 2.

$$1 \qquad 7$$

$$\times$$

$$1 \qquad 4$$

b. Then "by the cross," multiply 1 by 4 and 7 by 1. Adding these results, 4 + 7, we get 11. Now add the 2 from the previous computation: 11 + 2 = 13. Write the 3 to the left of the 8 and retain the 1.

c. Finally, multiply the 1's together: $1 \times 1 = 1$. Add the 1 that has been retained from the previous computation: 1 + 1 = 2. Write this 2 to the left of the 3. Thus the answer is 238.

2. This method may seem confusing, but it is really easy. Follow the steps above to find these products:

$$56 \times 82 \qquad\qquad 25 \times 34 \qquad\qquad 81 \times 43$$

For finding the products of numbers with more digits, 15th-century mathematicians employed several different schemes or algorithms. The word *algorithm* comes from the Latin rendering of the name of the great Arabic mathematician al-Khwarizmi (ca. 800–847), the author of the principal works that exposed Europeans to the Hindu-Arabic numerals and their methods of computation.

One of the most popular 15th-century algorithms for multiplication was the *gelosia* method, as Luca Pacioli (ca. 1494) explained in his popular arithmetic book:

> *By gelosia we understand the grating which is the custom to place at the windows of houses where ladies or nuns reside, so they cannot be early seen. Many such abound in the noble city of Venice.*

Our word *jealousy* is related to the word *gelosia*. Can you figure out why these words are related?

In the *Treviso Arithmetic* of 1478, the product 934×314 is found to be 293,276 by the gelosia method:

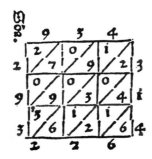

Let's examine just how the multiplication works.

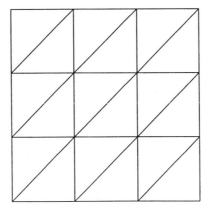

a. First construct a grid composed of square cells. For this grid the number of columns corresponds to the number of digits in one factor of the product, and the number of rows corresponds to the number of digits in the other factor. Each small cell is divided by a diagonal line extending from the upper right to the lower left.

b. To find the product of 372 × 431, one number (372) is written across the top of the grid; the other (431) is written down the right side.

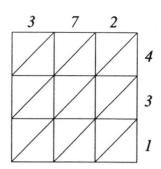

c. Now the product of each row number and column number is computed and written in the particular cell shared by the row and the column. The individual products are written with their tens digit above the diagonal line and their units digit below the line.

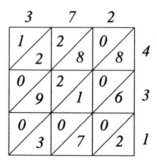

d. Starting at the lower right corner of the grid, sum the entries along each diagonal path within the grid. Write the units result at the end of each diagonal path and carry the tens digit to the path above and proceed in the same manner. When you are finished summing, the product is then read along the left and bottom edge of the grid: 160,332.

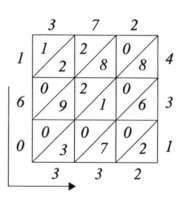

Study the last illustration carefully. Do you understand how the gelosia is set up and the product of the two numbers is found? If not, reread the above steps.

3. When you understand the algorithm, find the following products using the gelosia technique:

567 × 249   956 × 956   4,837 × 831   45.3 × 7.18

Can the gelosia method be used for finding the product of two numbers of any size?

4. **Library research:** The gelosia method of multiplication appeared in Europe in about the 14th century. It was transmitted through Arab arithmetic books—but transmitted from where? Who were the originators of this method of multiplication?

Medieval Multiplication—Teacher's Guide

Mathematical learning objective: provide practice with several historical multiplication algorithms

Materials needed: paper and pencil

Notes and suggestions: This activity should be done in stages, with the results discussed in class. It should become obvious that over the years, people have constantly been seeking better—i.e., easier and more efficient—ways to do computation. Our use of hand calculators and computers is just a phase of this evolution.

1. Students should be familiar with the Pythagorean table, although they may know it as a table of basic multiplication facts.

    The products of the numbers in the first row and first column can be read at the intersection of the row and column.

    Thus $7 \times 6 = 42$. The diagonal line represents the fact that the half of the table above the line is the same as the half of the table below the line. Today we would say that multiplication is a commutative operation—$a \times b = b \times a$.

2.
$$
\begin{array}{ccc}
5 & & 6 \\
& \times & \\
8 & & 2
\end{array}
\qquad
\begin{array}{l}
6 \times 2 = 12 \\
2 \times 5 = 10 \\
8 \times 6 = 48 \\
\underline{8 \times 5 = 40} \\
4{,}592
\end{array}
\qquad\qquad
\begin{array}{ccc}
2 & & 5 \\
& \times & \\
3 & & 4
\end{array}
\qquad
\begin{array}{l}
5 \times 4 = 20 \\
2 \times 4 = 8 \\
3 \times 5 = 15 \\
\underline{3 \times 2 = 6} \\
850
\end{array}
$$

$$
\begin{array}{ccc}
8 & & 1 \\
& \times & \\
4 & & 3
\end{array}
\qquad
\begin{array}{l}
1 \times 3 = 3 \\
8 \times 3 = 24 \\
4 \times 1 = 4 \\
\underline{8 \times 4 = 32} \\
3{,}483
\end{array}
$$

3.

    $567 \times 249 = 141{,}183$

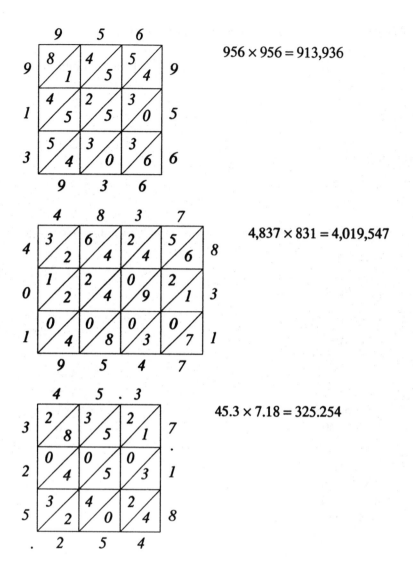

$956 \times 956 = 913{,}936$

$4{,}837 \times 831 = 4{,}019{,}547$

$45.3 \times 7.18 = 325.254$

Yes, the gelosia method can be used for finding the product of any two numbers.

4. It is believed that the gelosia method of multiplication originated in India and was transmitted westward by Arab traders.

HLT 12

Rabdologia

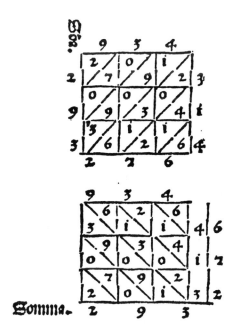

The difficulty and prolixity of calculation, the weariness of which is so apt to deter from the study of mathematics, I have always, with what little powers and little genius I possess, laboured to eradicate.

—*John Napier*

In the early Renaissance, the appearance of new computational techniques such as the gelosia method of multiplication, depicted above, did much to improve the ease and speed of numerical computation. But with the advent of a scientific spirit and a rapid increase of technological advances, an even more efficient means of performing computations was sought. A Scotsman, John Napier (1550–1617), noted that the numerical entries in the gelosia columns were merely multiples of the number that headed the column. Why not inscribe such columns of multiples on a set of rods and move the rods around to perform a needed multipli-

185

cation? Thus Napier converted a computation algorithm into a mechanical computing device. Napier called his invention "Rabdologia," from the Greek meaning "a collection of rods." However, the device soon assumed the popular name "Napier's rods" or "Napier's bones," as the more expensive sets were made of bone.

Let's see how this simple computer works by examining how to obtain the product 354 × 8.

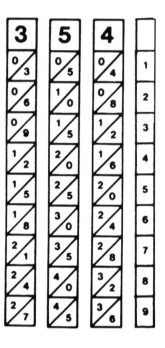

a. Select the 3, 5, and 4 rods and place them side by side so that the number 354 reads across the top. Along the right-hand side of this configuration, place the index rod, which contains the numbers 1 through 9.

b. To find the product 354 × 8, read along the row designated by 8 on the index rod.

c. Add the numbers within each diagonal path, as in the gelosia technique. The row shows that the product of 354 × 8 is 2,832.

To find the product of two multidigit numbers, you find several partial products and then sum them to obtain the desired product. For example, using the illustration, let's find the product of 354 × 628. To do this envision the multiplication as consisting of three separate products combined:

$$354 \times 8$$
$$354 \times 20$$
$$354 \times 600$$

Use the rods to obtain the units product in each case, adding appropriate 0's to the result to indicate what power of 10 is involved:

$$354 \times 8 = 2{,}832 \times 1 \quad = \quad 2{,}832$$
$$354 \times 2 = \quad 708 \times 1\,0 = \quad 7{,}080$$
$$354 \times 6 = 2{,}124 \times 100 = 212{,}400$$
$$\text{result: } \overline{222{,}312}$$

1. Using scissors, cut out the set of Napier's rods given on the last page of this activity. Compute the following products with these rods.

   a. 127 × 83

   b. 329 × 566

   c. 5,016 × 125

   d. 4,328 × 56.7

The concept of Napier's rods became the basis for the design of several later computers. By 1668 the rods had been made more versatile by being inscribed on cylinders which, in turn, were mounted in a box; by spinning a cylinder, the appropriate digits for the multiplicand could be chosen.

By 1885 two French mathematicians, Édouard Lucas and Henri Genaille, had perfected a variation of Napier's rods where the need to carry digits during the process of finding a partial product was eliminated. The following example demonstrates how the Genaille-Lucas rods function. We'll find the product of 3,271 × 4.

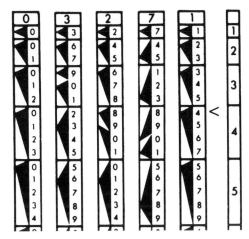

a. Select the 0, 3, 2, 7, and 1 rods and arrange them as shown at the right.

b. Place the index rod to the right of the configuration just as you would do using regular Napier's rods.

c. Read across from the 4 on the index rod, beginning with the first number in the first cell.

d. Then follow the arrows across the configuration, reading the numbers at each consecutive arrow—i.e., 13084. Thus: 3,271 × 4 = 13,084.

2. Cut out the set of Genaille-Lucas rods given at the end of this activity and use them to obtain these products:

   a. 129 × 43   b. 7,608 × 317   c. 14.25 × 39.8

3. **Library research:**

   a. John Napier was a talented mathematician skilled in many fields. His major mathematical accomplishment was not the invention of his Rabdologia. What is he most noted for in the history of mathematics?

   b. Since multiplication and division are opposite or inverse operations, it would seem that a set of rods could be invented to do division. Was such a set of rods ever invented?

   Learning Activities from the History of Mathematics

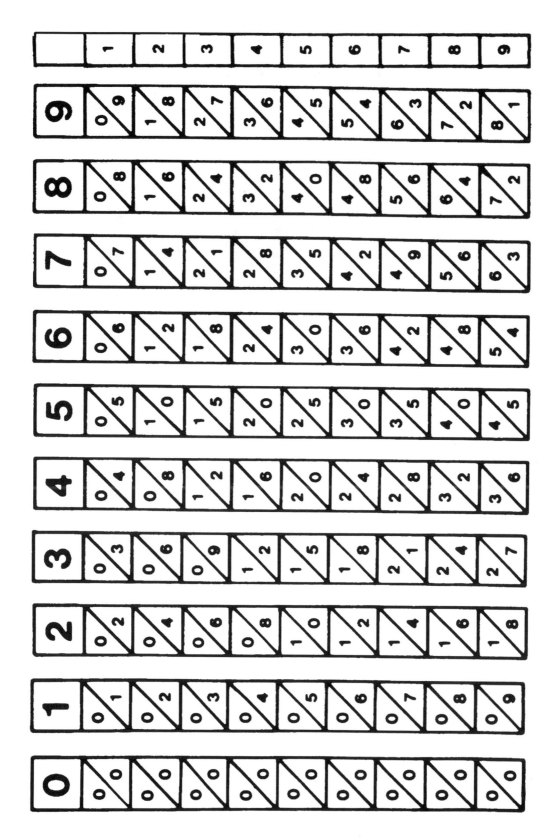

Napier's Rods

Name _____   Date _____

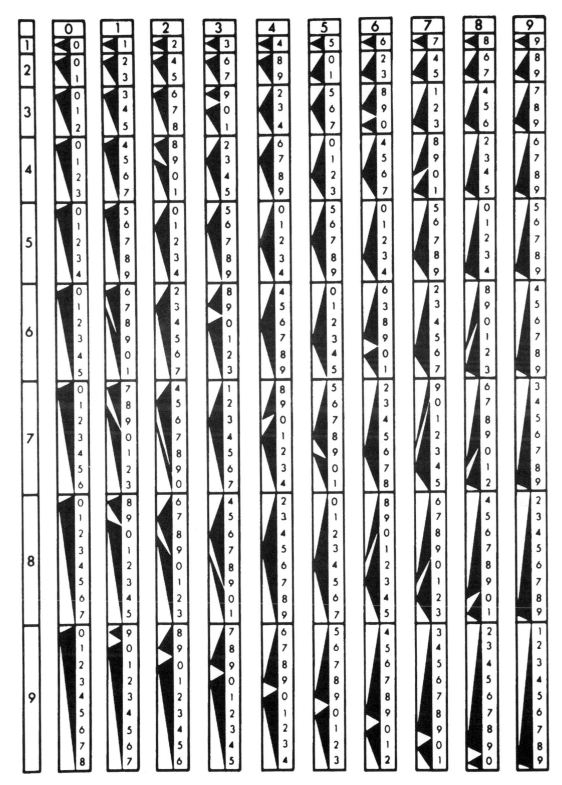

Genaille-Lucas Rods

Learning Activities from the History of Mathematics

Rabdologia—Teacher's Guide

Mathematical learning objective: perform multiplication using two early computing devices: Napier's bones and Genaille-Lucas rods; become familiar with simple analogue computers

Materials needed: scissors

Notes and suggestions: This exercise exposes students to simple analogue computers and helps them realize the fact that computers of various forms have been used for hundreds of years. If you want to provide students with more historical experience with computers, you can easily devise simple exercises employing a slide rule. A simple slide rule for adding and subtracting can be formed by using two rulers.

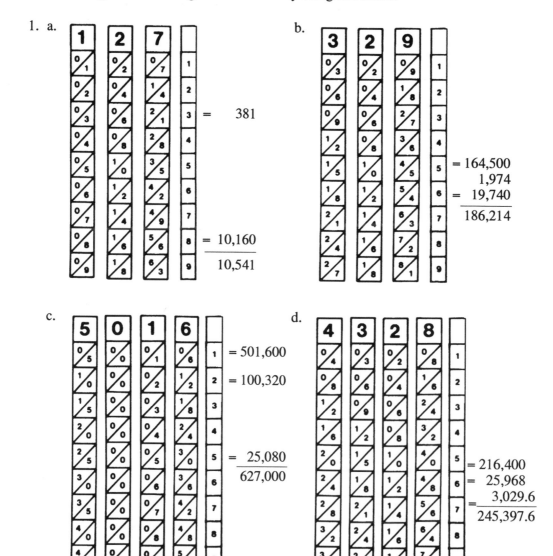

1. a.

= 381

= 10,160
_____
10,541

b.

= 164,500
    1,974
= 19,740
_____
186,214

c.

= 501,600
= 100,320

= 25,080
_____
627,000

d.

= 216,400
= 25,968
    3,029.6
_____
245,397.6

2. a.

b.

= 387

= 5,160

———

5,547

= 76,080

= 2,282,400

= 53,256

———

2,411,736

c.

= 427.50

= 11.400

= 128.25
_____
567.150

3. Library research will reveal that: (a) John Napier is best known for developing a system of logarithms and (b) Lucas and Genaille also devised a system of division rods.

HLT 13

Pi Is . . .

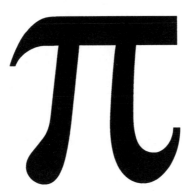

Webster's New World Dictionary defines *pi* as "the symbol π designating the ratio of the circumference of a circle to its diameter." While this definition is mathematically correct, it reflects little of the importance of π. Pi is a number, a universal constant that appears over and over again in many diverse mathematical situations. In fact, it may honestly be said that pi is one of the most important numbers that exists. From very early times, people have attempted to estimate the value of π. Many early peoples such as the Babylonians, Indians, and Chinese used a value of 3 as a general estimate of π.

1. A problem in the Egyptian Rhind papyrus, which was written in about 1650 B.C., seems to indicate that mathematicians of that time computed the area of a circle by taking ⁸⁄₉ the area of a square circumscribed about the circle. Using this technique and knowing the modern formula for the area of a circle, $A = \pi R^2$, what value for π did the ancient Egyptians use?

2. Following Webster's definition of π, let's approximate our own value for this mysterious number. Collect five circular objects such as jar lids, drinking cups, paper rolls, and empty food cans. Using a ruler and a piece of string, carefully measure the diameter, *D*, and the circumference, *C*, of each object. Measure the diameter by placing the ruler across the widest part of each circle. Measure the circumference by wrapping the string around each circle and then stretching the string straight and measuring it with a ruler. Record each measurement in the appropriate columns of the following table.

C	D	C/D

When you have recorded the values of C and D for five different objects, then use a calculator to compute the quotient C/D and record this value in the last column.

    a. Is there a pattern for the values of C/D?

    b. Obtain an average value for your computed values of C/D. What is it?

    c. This is your estimated value of π. How does it compare with the Egyptian value?

3. Throughout history many famous mathematicians have attempted to obtain accurate estimates for π. Use a calculator and compute how successful the following mathematicians were in their efforts. Convert their values, given here as common fractions, to decimals and compare the findings to decide who was the least and who was the most accurate.

    a. Archimedes (240 B.C.) $^{223}/_{71}$

    b. Claudius Ptolemy (A.D. 150) $^{377}/_{120}$

    c. Tsu Ch'ung-chih (A.D. 480) $^{355}/_{113}$

    d. Aryabhata I (A.D. 530) $^{62,832}/_{20,000}$

    e. Bhāskara II (A.D. 1150) $^{3,927}/_{1,250}$

    f. Fibonacci (A.D. 1202) $^{865}/_{275}$

4. The British mathematician John Wallis (1616–1703) used an infinite product to estimate π:

$$\pi = 4\left(\frac{2 \cdot 4 \cdot 4 \cdot 6 \cdot 6 \cdot 8 \cdot \;\;\cdot\;\;\cdot}{3 \cdot 3 \cdot 5 \cdot 5 \cdot 7 \cdot 7 \cdot \;\;\cdot\;\;\cdot}\right)$$

Extend the expression to 15 entries in both the numerator and the denominator. Then, using a calculator, compute the resulting value for π.

One of the most interesting and unusual methods for estimating π was discovered by the French mathematician Georges Louis Leclerc, the Comte de Buffon (1707–1788), commonly known as Buffon. Among his mathematical accomplishments he studied this problem:

If a large plane was covered with parallel lines drawn a distance apart, and if a needle of length l < a *was dropped repeatedly on this plane, what would be the probability that the needle would fall on a line?*

Buffon concluded that the probability, *P*, of the needle landing on a line was given by the expression:

$$P = \frac{2l}{\pi a}$$

If you conduct the experiment and drop the needle many times, *N*, on the lined plane and record the number of line crossings, *C*, you can compute *P* with this equation:

$$P = \frac{C}{N}$$

So you can obtain an estimate for π:

$$P = \frac{C}{N} = \frac{2l}{\pi a} \text{ or } \pi = \frac{2Nl}{Ca}$$

In 1901 the Italian mathematician Loazzerini estimated π correctly to six decimal places with 3,408 drops of a needle.

5. Use the following computer program to simulate Buffon's needle experiment and estimate π by permitting the computer to toss a needle 12,000 times. Even for a microcomputer, this experiment takes a little time—approximately 15 minutes on an Apple IIe.

```
 10  REM BUFFON'S NEEDLE EXPERIMENT
 20  N = 0
 30  HTAB 10: PRINT "BUFFON'S NEEDLE EXPERIMENT"
 40  PRINT: PRINT
 50  HTAB 5: PRINT "THROWS";
 60  HTAB 20: PRINT "ESTIMATE"
 70  PRINT: PRINT
 80  FOR J = 1 TO 24
 90  FOR K = 1 TO 500
100  X = RND (1)
110  U = SIN (3.1415927 * RND (1))
120  IF X > U THEN 140
130  N = N + 1
140  NEXT K
150  T = 500 * J
160  P = 2 * T/N
170  HTAB 5: PRINT T;
180  HTAB 20: PRINT P
190  NEXT J
200  END
```

How accurate is your result?

Pi—π

3.141592653589793238
462643383279502884
197169399375105820
974944592307816
406286208998628034
825342117067982148
086513282306647093
844609550582231725
359408128481117450
284102701938521105
596446229489549303
819644288109756659
334461284756482337
86783165 . . .

Pi Is . . .—Teacher's Guide

Mathematical learning objective: collect and process data and learn to estimate a value for π

Materials needed: string; ruler; a variety of small circular objects (jar lids, drinking glasses, etc.); calculator; computer

Notes and suggestions: These activities, while supplying practice in data collection and processing, should also impress on students the approximate nature of π—that the values we have are estimates.

1.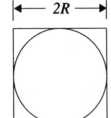

    Area of square $= 4R^2$

    $$\pi R^2 = \left(\frac{8}{9}\right) 4R^2$$

    Egyptian value for $\pi = \dfrac{32}{9} = 3.\overline{55}$

2. Depending on the objects measured, the input data will vary; however, the results should be similar. Here is a sample:

C	D	C/D
$10\frac{1}{2}$" (coffee cup)	$2\frac{15}{16}$"	3.574
$12\frac{1}{4}$" (coffee tin)	$3\frac{7}{8}$"	3.161
$2\frac{1}{4}$" (marker)	$\frac{11}{16}$"	3.27
7" (soda can)	$2\frac{5}{16}$"	3.027
$7\frac{5}{8}$" (drinking glass)	$2\frac{1}{2}$"	3.05

    For the same table:

    a. C/D is 3. something.

    b. Average value is 3.216

    c. This value is more accurate than the Egyptian value.

3. a. Archimedes, $\pi = 3.140845$

    b. Ptolemy, $\pi = 3.141\overline{66}$

    c. Tsu, $\pi = 3.1415\overline{92}$

    d. Aryabhata, $\pi = 3.1416$

    e. Bhāskara, $\pi = 3.1416$

f. Fibonacci, $\pi = 3.1\overline{45}$

4. Wallis's value

$$\pi = \frac{(2 \cdot 4 \cdot 4 \cdot 6 \cdot 6 \cdot 8 \cdot 8 \cdot 10 \cdot 10 \cdot 12 \cdot 12 \cdot 14 \cdot 14 \cdot 16 \cdot 16 \cdot \ \cdot \ \cdot \ )}{(3 \cdot 3 \cdot 5 \cdot 5 \cdot 7 \cdot 7 \cdot 9 \cdot 9 \cdot 11 \cdot 11 \cdot 13 \cdot 13 \cdot 15 \cdot 15 \cdot 17 \cdot \ \cdot \ \cdot \ )}$$

$$\pi = 3.0506$$

5. This experiment can be done by students actually dropping a needle or toothpick on the floor where lines have been drawn.

For $N = 12,000$, I obtained the value $\pi = 3.14836679$.

HLT 14

Shadow Reckoning

The first historically known mathematician is Thales of Miletus, who lived between the years 640 to 546 B.C. He was a Greek merchant who traveled widely in the Mediterranean region. During his travels, he learned the mathematics used in neighboring countries and brought this mathematics back to Greece, where he and his students expanded and perfected it. Thales was particularly impressed by the use of geometry for land surveying that he had observed in Egypt. One of his mathematical accomplishments that has been recorded in history is his use of geometry and shadows to measure the height of the Great Pyramid in Egypt.

Consider Thales' method. He knew that the length of the base of the Great Pyramid was 756 feet; at a certain time of the day, the pyramid cast a shadow 720 feet long. Thales placed a vertical staff at the end of this shadow and found that his 6-foot staff made a shadow 9 feet long.

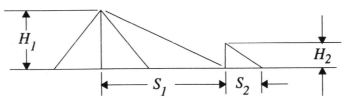

Using properties of similar right triangles, he then reasoned:

$$\frac{\text{height of pyramid}}{\text{length of pyramid's shadow}} = \frac{\text{height of staff}}{\text{length of staff's shadow}}$$

199

From this he found:

$$\text{height of pyramid} = \frac{(\text{pyramid's shadow length}) \, (\text{height of staff})}{\text{length of staff's shadow}}$$

or

$$\text{height of pyramid} = \frac{(720) \, (6)}{(9)} = 480 \text{ feet}$$

Thus by employing shadow reckoning based on simple geometric properties, Thales was able to measure an inaccessible distance, an impressive feat for his time and a demonstration of the power and usefulness of mathematics.

1. Use shadow reckoning to determine the following heights:

   a. your school building.

   b. a flagpole. (Check the accuracy of your estimate by measuring the length of the pole's rope or asking the people who maintain the flag and its pole.)

   c. a lamp pole or telephone pole. (Check your result by telephoning the electric company or the telephone company and asking the lengths of the poles in question.)

2. Thales' work with right triangles can be considered an early form of trigonometry. After all, trigonometry did evolve from shadow-reckoning activities. In his work with the pyramid, Thales used a ratio of height to base for a right triangle. Today, we would say he employed a trigonometric function. Which trigonometric function did Thales employ over 2,000 years ago?

Shadow Reckoning—Teacher's Guide

Mathematical learning objective: obtain practice in measuring, data collection, and simple geometric problem-solving

Materials: measuring tape or long string that can be accurately measured after being strung out

Notes and suggestions: These measuring exercises are excellent small-group activities for three to five students. Student teams can independently obtain estimates for the required heights and discuss their results in class.

1. Student results will vary depending on the situation.

2. Thales was making use of a ratio that we would recognize today as the tangent of an angle. In the early shadow-reckoning work, both tangent and cotangent ratios were used. The Egyptians had a special name for their cotangent function. They called it the *seqt*.

HLT 15

Measuring the World

Popular history reminds us that through the Middle Ages most people thought that the world was flat. Christopher Columbus is credited with dispelling this myth by making his epic journey to the East, finding a sea passage to the Americas, and in the process not falling off the end of the earth. Actually, it was known that the earth is round long before the time of Columbus. In fact the Greek astronomer–mathematician Eratosthenes, who lived about 230 B.C., computed the circumference of the earth. His method is quite simple.

Eratosthenes lived in the city of Alexandria in Egypt. He noted that when the midsummer sun was directly overhead at noon in the city of Syene, its rays at the same time were striking the city of Alexandria at an angle of 7°12'. Eratosthenes knew that the distance between these two cities was 5,000 *stadia*. He reasoned that if the earth was round, 7°12' = $\frac{1}{50}$ of 360°. Therefore 5,000 *stadia* = $\frac{1}{50}$ the circumference of the earth, and thus the circumference was 250,000 *stadia*.

1. In modern units of measurement Eratosthenes' *stadium* (singular for *stadia*) is 516.73 feet. What do you associate the word stadium with? Research the origin of this word to determine its mathematical connection with its modern usage.

2. How accurate was Eratosthenes' estimate for the circumference of the earth? What was the percentage of error in his calculation?

Consider the following variation of Eratosthenes' experiment. Assume that the sun is so far away from the earth that its rays effectively hit the earth as parallel lines. Then if two posts or staffs are set up along a north-south line on the earth and vertically placed in the ground, the angles their shadows, θ and ϕ respectively, make with the surface of the earth provide a measure of the incidence of the sun's rays. Then if D, the distance between the posts is known, the circumference of the earth, C, can be found by using this relationship:

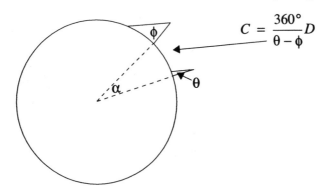

$$C = \frac{360°}{\theta - \phi} D$$

The measure for angles θ and ϕ can be determined by knowing the lengths of the vertical staffs, L_1 and L_2, and by accurately measuring the lengths of their respective shadows, S_1 and S_2:

$$\theta = \tan^{-1}\frac{L_1}{S_1} \text{ and } \phi = \tan^{-1}\frac{L_2}{S_2}$$

3. Refer to the diagram above and geometrically prove that

$m(\angle \theta) - m(\angle \phi) = m(\angle \alpha)$.

4. Use this technique of shadow reckoning to obtain your own estimate for the circumference of the earth. With the help of a map, locate a school district some distance away and north of your school's location. Contact a science or mathematics class in that school district and ask for their assistance. On your school grounds and your partner's school grounds, erect a vertical staff. Use a carpenter's level to assure the staff stands vertically. (You can easily erect a 2" × 2" staff with a height 4' to 6', or perhaps you can use a standing pole, such as a flagpole if you know its height.) On five consecutive days at a specified time around noon, observers are to measure the lengths of the shadows cast by the staffs and compute values for θ and ϕ. At the end of this period you will average the five individual values of angle measure and decide on a representative value for θ and ϕ. Compute the distance, D, between schools and apply the formula to obtain the circumference of the earth.

Measuring the World—Teacher's Guide

Mathematical learning objective: provide practice in measurement, data collection, and simple geometric problem-solving

Materials required: $2'' \times 2'' \times 6'$ staff; carpenter's level; measuring tape

Notes and suggestions: This activity should be performed as a class exercise. Students (and teachers) will be impressed that, with simple instruments and some basic mathematical knowledge, they can actually estimate the circumference of the earth. A local newspaper or television channel may wish to report on the class findings.

1. Today, the word *stadium* is associated with sports—a sports stadium. In ancient Greece a *stadium* was the distance a man could run at full speed. For the Greeks of Athens this was 630 feet. Eventually the track and spectator stands that were built for foot races were called a *stadium*. The *stadium* became a unit of length in the ancient world and varied according to location. Eratosthenes lived and worked in Egypt. The Egyptian *stadium* was 516.73 feet.

2. The equatorial circumference of the earth is 24,901.55 miles; Eratosthenes' result was 24,662 miles. His calculation was 239.55 miles less than the actual value, an error of .9%.

3.

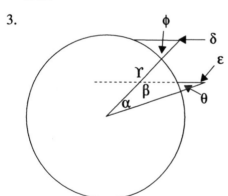

To prove: $m(\angle \theta) - m(\angle \phi) = m(\angle \alpha)$

$m(\angle \Upsilon) + m(\angle \delta) = 180°$	interior $\angle$'s on same side of transversal
$m(\angle \Upsilon) = m(\angle \beta)$	vertical angles
$m(\angle \beta) + m(\angle \delta) = 180°$	substitution
$m(\angle \alpha) + m(\angle \beta) + m(\angle \varepsilon) = 180°$	sum of $\angle$'s of triangle
$m(\angle \alpha) + m(\angle \varepsilon) = m(\angle \delta)$	
$m(\angle \alpha) = m(\angle \delta) - m(\angle \varepsilon)$	
$m(\angle \delta) = 90 - m(\angle \phi)$	acute $\angle$'s of right triangle
$m(\angle \varepsilon) = 90 - m(\angle \theta)$	
$m(\angle \delta) - m(\angle \varepsilon) = m(\angle \theta) - m(\angle \phi)$	
$\therefore\ m(\angle \alpha) = m(\angle \theta) - m(\angle \phi)$	

4. Results will vary. The results of one cooperative project are given below. Measurements were taken at 12:30 P.M. on five consecutive days.

location:		Pontiac, MI		Gainesville, FL
length of staff:		64"		95.9"
length of shadow:		121.5"		109.5"
$\tan \phi$	=	.5268	$\tan \theta =$	.8758
ϕ	=	27°47'	$\theta =$	41°13'

The distance between these cities is 933 miles.

The circumference of the earth is found to be 25,004 miles, a less than 1% error.

HLT 16

Measuring Angles

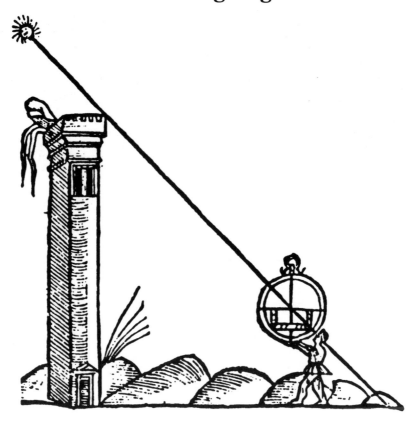

For thousands of years, people have used shadow reckoning to determine the heights of inaccessible objects or to locate points in the sky. In making such calculations or taking such sightings, a concept of angle was always involved; however, it took a long time before an angle was itself considered a mathematical entity that could be used in computing and to which properties could be assigned.

The ancient Greeks developed an instrument for angle-based sightings. It was called an *astrolabe*, which in Greek means "taking of the stars" and refers to the instrument's use in locating and recording the position of stars in the night sky. An astrolabe is a simple circular disc that is held aloft by a ring fixed to its edge. The weight of the astrolabe as it is held up by the ring helps to align the instrument in a vertical plane. Sightings are then taken along a movable bar fixed to the instrument's center. Once the sighting is established, the sighting bar's inclination can be read from a fixed reference scale on the astrolabe's surface.

The Greeks used their astrolabes for astronomy and land surveying work. When the Greek civilization fell into decline, knowledge and use of the astrolabe were passed on to the Arabs. Later, in the Middle Ages, European mathematicians learned about the astrolabe from Arab sources and again began using it in their work. Soon this instrument and variations of it were adapted for various mathematical situations, and the angle as a mathematical entity became recognized for its importance.

1. Let's construct a simple variation of the astrolabe called a clinometer. A clinometer measures inclination.

   a. Take a piece of cardboard about $8\frac{1}{2}" \times 11"$ and lay it flat so that its long side is at the top as shown below. About $\frac{1}{4}"$ from the right edge, draw a line parallel to the edge.

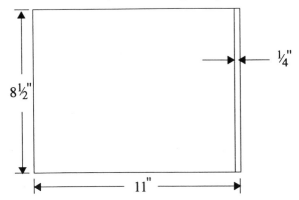

   b. Choose a point along the line about $\frac{1}{4}"$ down from the top edge. Make a hole through the cardboard at this point. Now place a protractor along the drawn line so that its reference line coincides with the drawn line and its center is over the hole. Then use this protractor to draw a scale, 0° to 90°, on the cardboard as shown.

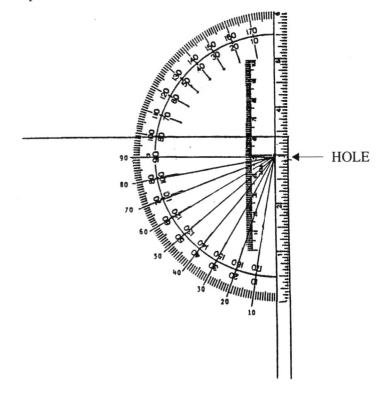

HOLE

Learning Activities from the History of Mathematics

c. Attach a string about a foot long from the hole in the cardboard. Weight the other end of the string with some paper clips or a metal washer. Tape a soda straw along the upper edge of the cardboard to serve as a sighting tube. Now by sighting through the straw at a distant elevated object and noting the angle β' as designated by the position of the string on the scale, you find the angle of the inclination, β, to the distant object.

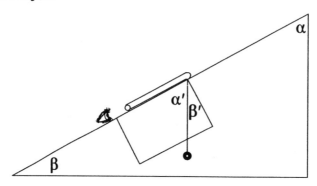

2. Use your knowledge of geometry to prove that $m(\angle\beta') = m(\angle\beta)$.

3. Use your clinometer to determine:

   a. the height of your school building.

   b. the height of another, taller building.

   c. the height of a tall tree or tower.

4. As shown in the picture below taken from a 16th-century mathematics book, you can use the clinometer to measure depth. Use your clinometer to determine the downward distance to some inaccessible object.

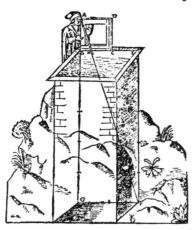

Measuring Angles—Teacher's Guide

Mathematical learning objective: use the properties of similar right triangles to obtain measurements of remote distances

Materials needed: string; washers or paper clips; soda straw; tape; protractor; cardboard

Notes and suggestions: Each student can make her or his own astrolabe.

1. This activity will take two periods of class time: one period for constructing the astrolabe, and another for finding required measurements and discussing results.

2.

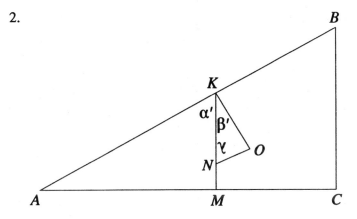

In $\triangle KNO$, $\triangle ABC$ $AB \| NO$

$m(\angle\beta) + m(\angle\alpha') = 90$	acute angles of right triangle
$m(\angle\Upsilon) + m(\angle\beta') = 90$	
$m(\angle\alpha') = m(\angle\Upsilon)$	alternate interior $\angle$'s
$\triangle KNO \approx \triangle ABC$	(AAA)
$m(\angle\beta) = m(\angle\beta')$	corresponding angle of similar $\triangle$'s

3. Results will vary according to situation.

4. Results will vary according to situation.

HLT 17

The *Lo Shu*

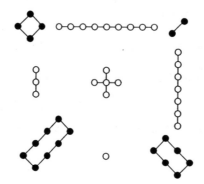

A legend in China tells that in about the year 2000 B.C. a magic turtle came out of the Yellow River and showed itself to Emperor Yu. On this turtle's back was a magic diagram composed of numbers. The Chinese called this diagram the *lo shu* and believed it contained many magic powers and was the source of all mathematics and science in China.

Above is a picture of the *lo shu* diagram. The numbers are represented as knots tied in black and white cords.

1. Use the grid at the right and write in the *lo shu* numbers. The resulting configuration is called a magic square. What is magic about it?

   Magic squares are classified by the numbers of rows and columns they have. This magic square is a 3 × 3 square. Another way of describing it is to say that it's of order 3.

   If a square's order is an odd number, it is said to be of odd order. If it is an even number, the square is said to be of even order. The *lo shu* is an odd-order magic square.

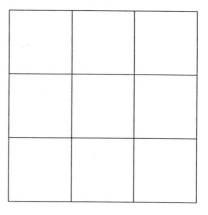

2. In any odd-order magic square, the central number is very important. Can you find a relationship among the magic property for the magic sum of the *lo shu*, the *lo shu*'s central number, and its order?

3. On an index card, draw the *lo shu* magic square. Rotate and turn your card. How many different magic squares can you generate by doing this? Note that a magic square is considered different if it has different numbers in a specific position, such as the upper right corner. Draw pictures of each square that you obtain.

4. Find a 3 × 3 magic square different from any of those that you found above.

5. Find a 3 × 3 magic square with a central number of 0.

6. Find a 3 × 3 magic square with all entries as fractions.

         Learning Activities from the History of Mathematics

The Lo Shu—*Teacher's Guide*

Mathematical learning objective: engage in numerical pattern recognition and apply simple algebraic and computational skills

Materials needed: index cards; blank paper

Notes and suggestions: This is an extremely fruitful topic from which to develop further activities. Students can explore higher-order magic squares. Students can learn how to construct their own magic squares aided by a calculator. They can investigate questions such as "Is the sum of two same-order magic squares also a magic square?"

1.

4	9	2
3	5	7
8	1	6

   The sums of all the row, column, and diagonal numbers are the same, 15.

2. Let S be the magic sum, C the value of the central number, and O the order. For all odd-order magic squares, $S = O \times C$.

3. Here students are performing permutations on a set of numbers. By physical movements or transformations they will find eight different magic squares with the central number 5.

4. Here students are pressed to find their own magic square. Encourage them to experiment. By adding, subtracting, multiplying, or dividing all entries in a magic square by the same number, another magic square is formed. Thus, from one magic square an infinite number of other squares can be found.

   Example:

4	9	2
3	5	7
8	1	6

$\times 2 =$

8	18	4
6	10	14
16	2	12

5.

4	9	2
3	5	7
8	1	6

$-5 =$

-1	4	-3
-2	0	2
3	-4	1

6.

4	9	2
3	5	7
8	1	6

$\div 12 =$

$\frac{1}{3}$	$\frac{3}{4}$	$\frac{1}{6}$
$\frac{1}{4}$	$\frac{5}{12}$	$\frac{7}{12}$
$\frac{2}{3}$	$\frac{1}{12}$	$\frac{1}{2}$

HLT 18

Squaring the Circle

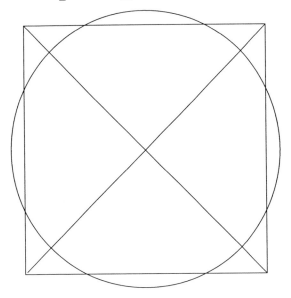

Among the geometric problems that concerned the ancient Greeks was the problem of "squaring the circle." Given a circle of known area, the problem was to construct a square of the same area using only a straightedge and compass. It was many years before it was proven that such a construction was impossible. However, the Greeks worked on this problem systematically and along the way found many interesting mathematical results. Let's examine some of these results.

1. Euclid in Proposition 14, Book II, of his *Elements* gives the following construction for squaring a rectangle: Given the rectangle *ABCD*, side *AB* is extended the length *CB* to point *E*. *AE* is used as a diameter to construct a semicircle. Side *BC* is now extended to meet this semicircle at point *F*. $\overline{BF}$ now supplies the side for the required square *BFGH*.

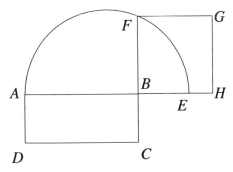

On a blank sheet of paper, construct a rectangle and carry out the above construction to find a square of the same area as the rectangle. Use your knowledge of algebra and geometry to prove that the square and the rectangle have the same area.

2. Use the knowledge obtained above to "square a triangle"; that is, construct a triangle and find a square of equal area by construction.

3. The Greek mathematician Hippocrates of Chios (ca. 440 B.C.), in his attempts to square the circle, invented a theory of lunes. The word *luna* in Latin means "the moon." Lunes are geometric figures formed by the intersection of two circular arcs. These figures or regions look like pieces of the moon. Hippocrates discovered that a particular lune could be found to possess the same area as a perscrible semisquare, and this relationship could be obtained by geometric constructions. Carry out Hippocrates' construction as follows and prove that the lune and the semisquare have the same area.

Construct a line segment *AB*. Using $\overline{AB}$ as a diameter, construct a semicircle. Mark the midpoint of $\overset{\frown}{AB}$, *C*, and draw $\overline{AC}$ and $\overline{CB}$. The isosceles triangle *ACB* forms a semisquare. Complete the square and label the fourth vertex, *D*. Using *D* as the center of a circle, draw an arc connecting *A* and *B*. The region *ACB* forms a lune. Now show that the area of this lune equals the area of triangle *ACB*.

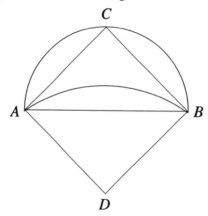

4. In the ancient Indian mathematical work called the *Sulvasutra* [*Cord Stretching Manual*], a method is given for constructing a circle with the same area as a given square. Perform this construction of "circling the square" and then calculate the area of the two figures and compare your results.

  a. Draw a square.

  b. Circumscribe this square with a circle.

  c. Construct a perpendicular bisector from the center of the square *O* through its upper side. The bisector intersects the upper side at point *P* and the circumscribing circle at point *M*.

  d. Divide $\overline{PM}$ into thirds. Let the division points be *K* and *N*, where *K* lies closer to point *P*.

  e. Use $\overline{OK}$ as a radius to construct a circle. This circle is supposed to have the same area as the original square.

  Does it?

Squaring the Circle—Teacher's Guide

Mathematical learning objective: obtain practice in geometric problem-solving

Materials needed: blank paper; ruler; compass

Notes and suggestions: This activity exposes the students to a classical problem of Greek geometry. It illustrates how solution attempts for a particular problem may generate further mathematical principles and concepts.

1. *Proof:* Let $BC = a$, $DC = b$; then the area of the rectangle $ABCD = ab$. Now construct $\overline{AF}$ and $\overline{FE}$; $\triangle AFB \sim \triangle AEB$. Therefore, $AB/BF = BF/BE$ and

    $$(BF)^2 = (AB)(BE)$$
    $$(BF)^2 = ab.$$

    The area of the constructed square is ab, the area of the rectangle.

    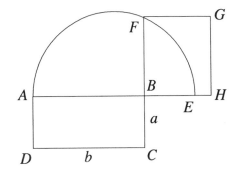

2. Let the triangle have base length b and height h. Students construct a rectangle of length b and width $h/2$ and apply the technique from problem 1.

3. There are many ways to obtain a proof. Here's one that depends on the fact that similar circular segments have areas proportional to the squares of their chords. Consider the semicircle divided into four areas: A_1, A_2, A_3, and A_4, as indicated by numbers. Then:

    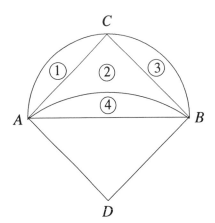

    $$A_1 = A_3, \quad \frac{A_4}{(AB)^2} = \frac{A_1}{(AC)^2} \quad \text{but } AC = \frac{\sqrt{2}}{2}(AB)$$

    Thus:

    $$\frac{A_4}{(AB)^2} = \frac{2A_1}{(AB)^2} \Rightarrow A_4 = 2A_1 = A_1 + A_3$$

    The lune is composed of areas $A_1 + A_2 + A_3$ and the half-square ACB areas $A_2 + A_4$, but $A_2 + A_4 = A_1 + A_2 + A_3$; therefore, the area of the lune is the same as the area of the half-square.

4. To compute the area of the resulting circle, let the side of the original square be S; therefore, its area is S^2. The radii of the inscribing circle will be of length $\dfrac{S\sqrt{2}}{2}$. Length of $\overline{MP} = \dfrac{S\sqrt{2}}{2} - \dfrac{S}{2}$

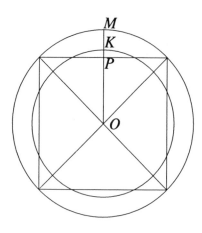

$$\frac{\overline{MP}}{3} = \frac{S}{6}(\sqrt{2}-1),\ OK = \frac{S}{2} + \frac{S}{6}(\sqrt{2}-1)$$

Area of circle with radii $OK =$

$$\frac{\pi\,(3S + S[\sqrt{2}-1])^2}{6} = 1.01724\ S^2\ 1.7\%\ \text{error}$$

However, this error is based on use of the modern value for π. The ancient Indians used an approximate value for π of 3. Under this assumption the error is less than $\frac{1}{2}\%$.

HLT 19

Regular Polygons

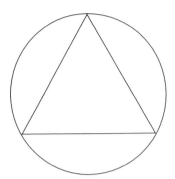
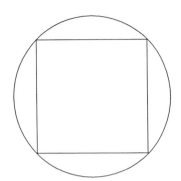
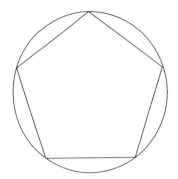

A polygon is a closed plane figure whose sides are composed of line segments. If the length of the polygon's sides are equal, it is called a regular polygon. Ancient Greek mathematicians investigated how regular polygons could be constructed using only a ruler and compass. They found that they could construct only four sets of such polygons. Euclid in the *Elements*, Book IV, describes how to construct regular polygons of three, four, five, six, and fifteen sides. Let's conduct our own investigations for constructing regular polygons.

1. On a blank sheet of paper, using a ruler and compass, construct an equilateral triangle whose sides are 3 inches long. Circumscribe this triangle with a circle. Construct a regular hexagon within this circle by constructing perpendicular bisectors to each side of the triangle; where the vertices of the triangle and the bisectors of its sides intersect the circle determines the sides for the hexagon. By repeating this process, what kind of regular polygons can you construct?

2. On a blank sheet of paper, construct a square of side 3 inches. Circumscribe the square with a circle. By bisecting the sides of the square you can construct an eight-sided polygon. Do it. What is the name of this polygon? Can you repeat this process of bisection to construct other regular polygons? If so, what kind of polygons do you obtain?

3. The Greek mathematician–astronomer Ptolemy, who lived about A.D. 150, devised a method for constructing a regular pentagon. We will use Ptolemy's method to construct a pentagon.

   On a blank sheet of paper, draw a circle of radius 3 inches. Label the center O. Construct a pair of perpendicular diameters of the circle—they will intersect at O.

   Label the points where the diameters intersect the circle A, B, C, and D. Bisect $\overline{OB}$ and call the point of bisection E. Using $\overline{AE}$ as a radius and E as a center, scribe an arc of a circle intersecting $\overline{OD}$ at point F. The distance AF supplies the length of the sides for the inscribed pentagon. Use this distance to construct the pentagon. If each side of this pentagon is bisected, what regular polygon can be formed? By repeating this process, what polygon can be obtained? If $OA = 1$, what is the length of FO?

Learning Activities from the History of Mathematics

4. The Greek technique for constructing a 15-sided regular polygon used both a regular pentagon and an equilateral triangle, as shown below:

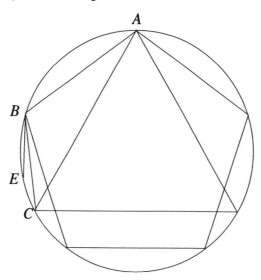

Let $\overline{AB}$ be a side of the pentagon as shown and $\overline{AC}$ be a side of the triangle. Construct $\overline{BC}$ and show that the perpendicular bisector of $\overline{BC}$ intersects the circle at point E and that $\overline{BE}$ will be a side of the required 15-sided regular polygon. Construct this polygon.

5. **Library Research:** In 1796 the German mathematician Carl Friedrich Gauss made a discovery concerning the construction of regular polygons. What was this discovery?

Regular Polygons—Teacher's Guide

Mathematical learning objective: investigate various properties of regular polygons; practice Euclidean constructions

Materials needed: unlined paper; ruler; drawing compass

Notes and suggestions: This activity familiarizes students with the properties of several regular polygons. You can build more specific, detailed lessons on the experience gained in these exercises. Note that to facilitate results, measuring lengths with a ruler is permitted.

1. Students should know how to construct an equilateral triangle. On a straight line, mark two points 3″ apart. Using these points as centers for a circle of radius 3″, scribe two circles. The points of intersection for the two circles mark the third vertex for the equilateral triangle:

   By repeated bisections, the students should realize that they can construct a family of regular $3(2^n)$-gons where $n = 0, 1, 2, \ldots$.

2. Students should know how to construct the square. After circumscribing it and bisecting its sides, the students obtain an 8-sided regular *octagon*. Repeated bisections result in producing the family of 2^K-gons where $K = 2, 3, \ldots$.

3. The construction is described in detail and will result in a regular pentagon; however, drawing accuracy can alter results. Approximate graphical results should be acceptable. Bisecting the sides produces the family of $5(2^n)$-gons where $n = 0, 1, 2, \ldots$. The length is $\dfrac{\sqrt{5}-1}{2}$, the golden ratio.

4. This technique is seldom seen and makes for an interesting mathematical exercise. The rationale for this construction is as follows:

   a. Arc AC is $\frac{1}{3}$ of the circle's circumference $\overset{\frown}{AB}$ is $\frac{1}{5}$ of the circle's circumference.

   b. Arc BC is their difference, $\frac{1}{3} - \frac{1}{5} = \frac{2}{15}$ of the circumference.

   c. Chord BC is drawn. The perpendicular bisector (radius) drawn to BC from the circle's center will also bisect $\overset{\frown}{BC}$ at point E.

   d. $\overline{BE}$ is the side of a regular 15-sided polygon.

   Note: Now by repeated bisecting of the sides of this polygon, the family of $15(2^n)$-gons where $n = 0, 1, 2, \ldots$ is generated.

5. **Library research:** Gauss discovered that regular polygons with a prime number of sides could be constructed only with a straightedge and compass if the number of sides could be given by the expression $2^{2^n} + 1$ for $n = 0, 1, 2, \ldots$. Thus, he established that regular polygons of 17, 257, and 65,537 could also theoretically be constructed.

HLT 20

Pascal's Triangle

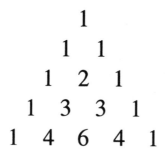

The table of numbers shown above is very important in the history of mathematics. It is usually called "Pascal's triangle," named after the French mathematician Blaise Pascal (1623–1662), who investigated many of its properties. This triangle and its interesting properties were known well before Pascal's time. The triangle was used around the year 1300 in China, and more than 500 years before Pascal was born, the Persian mathematician Omar Khayyám did computations using this triangle.

Let's investigate some of its numerical properties. First let's rewrite the triangle in another form.

1					row 0
1	1				row 1
1	2	1			row 2
1	3	3	1		row 3
1	4	6	4	1	row 4

In this form, the rows of numbers are clearly identified. Thus row 2 consists of the numbers 1, 2, 1.

1. Expand the following binomial expressions:

   $(a + b)^0$

   $(a + b)^1$

   $(a + b)^2$

   $(a + b)^3$

For each expression, compare the numerical coefficients obtained with the numbers in Pascal's triangle. What do you notice?

Learning Activities from the History of Mathematics

2. Pascal found a very simple pattern whereby every number in the triangle could be found as a sum of two adjacent numbers. Carefully study the numbers given in the triangle on the preceding page and determine a rule by which each number can be determined. Use this rule to extend the triangle to nine rows.

3. Use the information from your new triangle to expand quickly $(a + b)^5$ and $(a + b)^8$.

4. Find the sum of the numbers in each row. Do you see a pattern? Without writing out the 12th row, predict what the sum of its numbers would be.

5. In your triangle of numbers, choose any number other than a 1 on the left side. Move one position to the left of this number, then add all the numbers forming a column directly above the number where you are positioned. What do you find? Will this principle work for other numbers? Try it out and see.

6. Divide the numbers in each row by 2 and replace each number by its resulting remainder, either 0 or 1. Now carefully examine your new triangle of remainders. The 0's and 1's form patterns. In this new triangle, what is the next row that will appear similar to row 2? After that what is the next row that will appear similar to row 2? Can you find a rule to help us locate any row that will appear similar to the second row?

7. Throughout history many special sequences of numbers have been discovered and used. The Pythagoreans of ancient Greece had two special sets of numbers—

   the triangular numbers: 1, 3, 6, 10, 15, . . .

      and

   the tetrahedral numbers: 1, 4, 10, 20, . . .

   Can you find the triangular numbers and the tetrahedral numbers in your Pascal's triangle? If so, write down the next two numbers in each sequence.

8. The 13th-century Italian mathematician Leonardo of Pisa, sometimes called Fibonacci, discovered an interesting set of numbers that have now been named after him:

                    1, 1, 2, 3, 5, 8, . . .

   Carefully study these Fibonacci numbers. Can you find a method of finding the next few numbers? If so, write down the next four Fibonacci numbers.

   The Fibonacci numbers appear as special sums in the Pascal's triangle. Use your triangle to find out how to form these sums.

9. **Library research:** Why are the triangular numbers called "triangular"? Why are the tetrahedral numbers called "tetrahedral"?

Pascal's Triangle—Teacher's Guide

Mathematical learning objective: perform a binomial expansion assisted by Pascal's triangle; practice pattern recognition

Materials needed: paper and pencil

Notes and suggestions: Pascal's triangle is one of the most mathematically fascinating numerical tables ever devised. While it possesses many interesting properties, these properties are easy to discover. The suggested exercises reveal several of these properties; however, an ambitious student can find many others.

1. $(a + b)^0 = 1$

   $(a + b)^1 = 1a + 1b$

   $(a + b)^2 = 1 a^2 + 2 ab + 1 b^2$

   $(a + b)^3 = 1 a^3 + 3 a^2 b + 3ab^2 + 1 b^3$

   The coefficients for the 0 expansion match the number in the 0 row of the triangle, the coefficients for the 1 expansion match the numbers in the first row of the triangle, and so on. In other words, the triangle can supply the coefficients.

2. Both the left and the right sides of the triangle are composed of 1's. Any other number can be found as being the sum of the number directly above it and the number to the left of that number. For example: $3 = 2 + 1$; $6 = 3 + 3$.

									Row
1									0
1	1								1
1	2	1							2
1	3	3	1						3
1	4	6	4	1					4
1	5	10	10	5	1				5
1	6	15	20	15	6	1			6
1	7	21	35	35	21	7	1		7
1	8	28	56	70	56	28	8	1	8

3. $b)^5 = 1a^5 + 5a^4 b + 10a^3 b^2 + 10a^2 b^3 + 5ab^4 + 1b^5$

   $(a + b)^8 = 1a^8 + 8a^7 b + 28a^6 b^2 + 56a^5 b^3 + 70a^4 b^4 + 56a^3 b^5 + 28a^2 b^6 + 8ab^7 + 1b^8$

4. | row | sum |
    |-----|-----|
    | 0 | $1 = 2^0$ |
    | 1 | $2 = 2^1$ |
    | 2 | $4 = 2^2$ |
    | 3 | $8 = 2^3$ |
    | $\vdots$ | |
    | n | $= 2^n$ |

Sum for the 12th row is $2^{12} = 4{,}096$

5. The sum of the numbers in the column equals the number at which you began. This rule will work for any number.

6. When we divide the triangle's numbers by 2, the triangle of remainders becomes:

```
      1
     1 1          row 2 (all 1's) sum = 2
    1 0 1
   1 1 1 1        row 4 (all 1's) sum = 4
```

Rows 4 and 8 are similar to row 2

$$2^{n+1} = nth \quad \text{similar successor to row 2}$$

i.e. $\quad 2^{1+1} - 2^2 = 4 \quad$ 1st successor

$\qquad 2^{2+1} = 2^3 = 8 \quad$ 2nd successor

$\qquad\qquad$ etc.

7.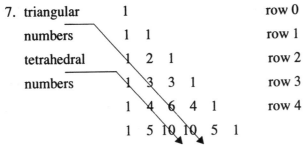

    triangular numbers: 1, 3, 6, 10, 15, <u>21</u>, <u>28</u>, . . .

    tetrahedral numbers: 1, 4, 10, 20, <u>35</u>, <u>56</u>, . . .

8. Each number is the sum of the two previous numbers.

    1, 1, 2, 3, 5, 8, <u>13</u>, <u>21</u>, <u>44</u>, <u>65</u>, . . .

    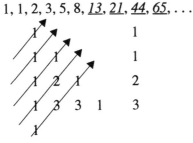

Sums of numbers along diagonals to the upper right will produce Fibonacci numbers.

9. **Library research:** Triangular numbers were conceived out of triangular configurations of dots:

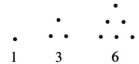

Now visualize these dots as marbles. Marbles can be piled up to form pyramids or tetrahedrons:

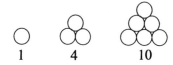

HLT 21

The Bridges of Koenigsberg

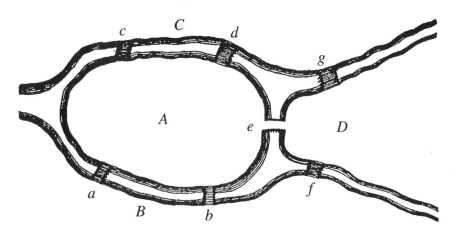

The Prussian city of Koenigsberg was built along the Pregel River. In fact, the city was located on both sides of the river and in the river on two islands. The islands were connected to each other and the rest of the city by a series of seven bridges. A favorite recreation for the people of Koenigsberg was to stroll across the bridges, visit the islands, and return home. As a result of this walking tour, a question was raised:

Is it possible for a person taking a Sunday stroll to follow a path that will allow him to cross each bridge once and only once?

Citizens of Koenigsberg tried various routes and decided that achieving such a walk was impossible.

The mathematician Leonhard Euler (1707–1783) heard of this problem and became interested in it. Euler drew a simple map of the situation noting the islands and the position of each bridge. Euler's diagram is shown at the top of this page. Using diagrams, Euler investigated the situation and found certain mathematical properties that determined if such a problem could be solved.

Learning Activities from the History of Mathematics

Let's investigate this problem using some of Euler's methods. First he drew a path indicating how a person would have to walk to cross all the bridges and visit the islands.

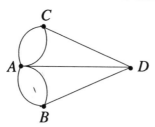

On this path, the letters *A*, *B*, *C*, and *D* represent the land masses, and the line segments or arcs represent the bridges. Euler then attempted to trace a path starting from one point and passing along all segments and arcs without repeating. He found that he could not do it—the path was not traceable or traversable. Euler then made simpler diagrams of different walking situations and investigated them in a similar manner. Some were possible, some were not. On the basis of these findings, he came to several mathematical conclusions.

Call a diagram of possible paths as Euler drew a *network*.

Each line in the network is a *path*, and each point into which two or more paths lead is called a *vertex*.

If a vertex connects an even number of paths, it is called an *even vertex*. If the number of paths is odd, the vertex is called an *odd vertex*.

1. Investigate the following networks. List their properties in the table below. Place a piece of tracing paper over each network and trace out the paths testing the network to see if it is traversable. Remember that in traversing a network, you may move through a vertex many times but are allowed to travel on a path only once.

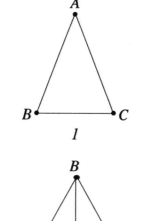

1

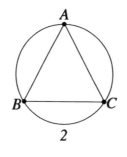

2

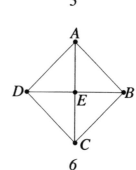

3

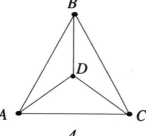

4

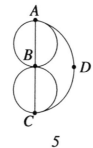

5

6

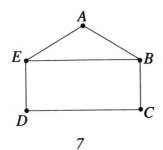

7

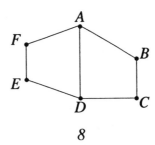

8

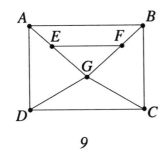

9

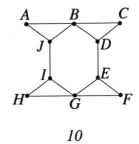

10

Network	Number of Vertices	Number of Odd Vertices	Number of Even Vertices	Can Network Be Traversed?
1				
2				
3				
4				
5				
6				
7				
8				
9				
10				

Euler found a relationship between the numbers of odd and even vertices in a network and its traversability. What relationships do you find from your data? Test these relationships by drawing other networks, and traverse them.

2. For the networks you tested above that are traversable, can you begin your travels at any vertex and still obtain a traversable path? If not, find a rule to tell someone where to begin traveling to traverse those networks.

3. Three factories are to be built in a city. Each factory must have gas, water, and electricity supplied from the gas plant, the power plant, and the waterworks. The supply lines for these utilities cannot cross each other. On a clean sheet of paper draw three factories and the gas plant, the power plant, and the waterworks. Draw the lines coming from each. Can you connect the utilities to the factories without crossing supply lines?

4. Charlie wishes to paint all the floors in a house. He hopes to go in one door, work his way across the floors of all the rooms (passing through each door only once), and leave through the back door. A floor plan of Charlie's house is given below. Can he do the job?

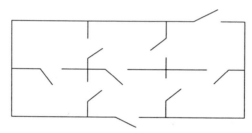

Learning Activities from the History of Mathematics

The Bridges of Koenigsberg—Teacher's Guide

Mathematical learning objective: become familiar with simple networks and undertake network analysis; form and test own hypothesis

Materials needed: tracing paper

Notes and suggestions: The Koenigsberg bridge problem sets the stage for enrichment activities involving networks and graph theory. Students enjoy the puzzlelike qualities of the problem. Within the guidance of this activity they should be able to discover some of the rules for traversability of a network. Following this exercise you can give students more formal work involving the planning of delivery or airline routes.

Network	Number of Vertices	Number of Odd Vertices	Number of Even Vertices	Can Network Be Traversed?
1	3	0	3	yes
2	3	0	3	yes
3	3	2	1	yes
4	4	4	0	no
5	4	0	4	yes
6	5	4	1	no
7	5	2	3	yes
8	6	2	4	yes
9	7	6	1	no
10	10	4	6	no

Conclusions:

a. Networks having only even vertices are traversable.

b. Networks with exactly two odd vertices are traversable.

c. Networks having more than two odd vertices are not traversable.

1. Networks 1, 2, 3, 5, 7, and 8 are traversable. Networks 1, 2, and 5 can be traversed starting at any vertex. Network 3 cannot be traversed by starting at vertex *C*; network 7 cannot be traversed by starting at vertices *A*, *D*, or *C*; network 8 can only be traversed by starting at either vertex *A* or *D*.

Conclusions:

a. A network with all even vertices can be traversed starting from any vertex.

b. A network with exactly two odd vertices can be traversed only by starting at an odd vertex.

2. The utilities cannot be connected to the factories as specified.

3. Yes, the network (rooms are vertices, doors are paths) has 5 even and 2 odd vertices. It is traversable.

CHAPTER 6

One Picture Is Worth . . .

A problem often encountered in teaching about the history of mathematics, and, indeed, about history in general, is its remoteness in time from present audiences. We are talking about mathematical events and discoveries that may have taken place hundreds, perhaps even thousands, of years ago. How can we help our students identify with these happenings? Of course, a good teacher tries to make the discussions themselves interesting and relevant, but words are limited in their impact, and frequently the remoteness remains as a psychological barrier to be overcome. One technique that helps to lessen this remoteness and instill a fuller appreciation of historical accomplishments is the use of visual evidence of the events under discussion, that is, pictures of the people involved, facsimiles of written works, or original diagrams and pictures or replications of artifacts such as clay tablets and early computers. Just as a good text on the history of mathematics occasionally refers to an illustration, so too should the classroom teacher employ visual and even tactile aids in discussing the history of mathematics.

Tactile aids are those that can be handled and manipulated by the students. For example, when I discuss the Babylonian cuneiform numeration system, I make "clay tablets" out of Plasticine modeling clay and pass them out to the class for deciphering. (Have you ever thought of how big such tablets were? They fit into the palm of your hand.) Next, I allow the students to erase the inscriptions (easy to do with Plasticine) and replace them with their own, and then pass the tablets to companions for deciphering. Similarly, I have produced tally sticks for financial negotiations and supplied patterns for each student to make a set of Napier's bones. Such aids are usually teacher-conceived, with their production and use depending on the knowledge and resourcefulness of individual teachers.

In the usual teaching circumstances, visual aids in the form of pictures, films, and videotapes are easier to obtain and use. Transparencies can be made from noteworthy and available pictures and illustrations. For example, in discussing the standardization of units of measure, I cite the instance of the 16th-century *rood* [rod], determined by the collective measurement of the left feet of 16 churchgoers selected randomly: "Bid sixteen men to stop, tall ones and short ones, as they happen to come out . . . ." At the same time I show a picture of the situation. The picture is actually a woodcut from a 16th-century surveying manual and stresses the use of correct procedures in establishing units of measurement.

This book contains a number of historical illustrations that can serve as transparency masters.

A good selection of historical posters and charts is available from commercial vendors, principally:

Carolina Biological Supply Company (Cabisco)
2700 York Road
Burlington, NC 27215-3398
Phone: 800-334-5551

Dale Seymour Publications
P.O. Box 10888
Palo Alto, CA 94303
Phone: 800-USA-1100

J. Weston Walch, Publisher
321 Valley Street
P.O. Box 658
Portland, ME 04104-0658
Phone: 800-341-6094

Occasionally, you can obtain free materials as a public service from large private corporations and companies. IBM Corporation has produced a most excellent "Men of Mathematics" chart. (Yes, they are acutely aware of the sexist implications of the title and may amend it in future editions.) Contact your local IBM representative concerning availability of copies. The Ford Motor Company offers an attractive "History of Measurement" chart. Address requests to:

Ford Motor Company
The American Road
Dearborn, MI 48121

Recently textbook publishers have been using historical material in their promotion of new mathematics texts. These materials are frequently distributed at vendor booths during professional meetings and conferences.

Among the variety of existing visual aids, I believe the most efficient in depicting a historical discovery or event in mathematics are films and videotapes. These media often feature the actual locations, artifacts, and writings of our mathematical ancestors and capture the color and spirit of the times. A selective listing of such media follows for your possible use.

A Selected Listing of Films and Videotapes

The following films and tapes are available on a rental basis from several film distribution centers and libraries. All are appropriate for use at the secondary school level. I have attempted to provide enough descriptive information on each so that you can make your own personal judgments as to the usefulness of the film or tape to your teaching needs. The information format for each entry is the same:

Title
Film or tape   Time
Brief description of contents
Producer if known   Date
Possible source

When many possible sources exist, only one or two principal suppliers are listed by abbreviation. These abbreviations are identified at the end of the list under "Sources."

1. *Algebra: Historical Introduction*
    16 mm film   28 min.
    Presents the three stages in the development of algebra: rhetorical, syncopated, and symbolic. Emphasizes historical importance of the Rhind papyrus (1650 B.C.), Diophantus' *Arithmetica* (ca. A.D. 250), and al-Khwarizmi's *al-jabr* (ca. A.D. 825).
    Modern Learning Aids   1963
    WU

2. *The Algebra of the Unknown*
    16 mm film   25 min.
    Details the history of analytic geometry and the development of coordinate geometry. Discusses plane, solid, and linear loci, graphs, and the development of notation and its use in solving equations and depicting curves. Looks at the history of mathematical reasoning from the early Greeks to Sir Isaac Newton's 72 types of cubic equations.
    The Open University   1974
    IU; O Kent U

3. *The Birth of Calculus*
    $\frac{1}{2}$" VHS   25 min.
    Analyzes the similarities and differences in the discovery and development of calculus independently by two mathematicians: Sir Isaac Newton in 1665–66 in England and Gottfried Wilhelm Leibniz some ten years later in Germany. Uses the original writings of both men for a glimpse into the process of discovery and the birth of calculus.
    The Open University   1986
    P.S.U.

4. *The Birth of Modern Geometry*
    $\frac{1}{2}$" VHS   25 min.
    Traces the development of geometry from the work of the early 17th-century monk

Marin Mersenne, through that of Descartes, Desargues, and Pascal. The revolutionary new method of calculating inspired Sir Isaac Newton and others to new mathematical discoveries in the latter half of the 17th century.
The Open University   1986
P.S.U.

5. *The Delian Problem*
   16 mm film   24 min.
   Lists the difficulties and traces the efforts at solutions to the Delian problem, so called because it first appeared in a legend of the Greek island of Delos. The problem, one of the three "classical problems" of antiquity, consists of producing a cube with twice the volume of a given cube. Shows the mechanical solution attributed to Plato, the reformulation of the problem by Hippocrates of Chios, and Menaechmus' solution by means of conic sections.
   The Open University   1974
   IU

6. *Donald in Mathmagic Land*
   16 mm film $\frac{1}{2}$" VHS   28 min.
   Uses cartoon characters, principally Donald Duck, to illustrate the mathematical basis of music, architecture, sculpture, and painting. Donald tours Mathmagic Land, where he first meets Pythagoras, father of mathematics and music, and discovers mathematical ratio in the musical scale. Donald's travels also expose him to the mathematical relationships found in nature, games, and art. The presentation uses a historical basis and shows how scientific progress depends on mathematics.
   Disney   1960
   P.S.U.

7. *The Emergence of Greek Mathematics*
   $\frac{1}{2}$" VHS   24 min.
   Euclid's *Elements* is one of the most reprinted books of all time. How did it come about and why does it remain a classic textbook? Starting with the concept of proof, which was a relatively new one in the 3rd century B.C., this presentation examines each of the 13 books in detail. It shows how this classic text has been passed down to us and how historians were able to re-create the original from later, amended editions.
   The Open University   1988
   P.S.U.

8. *The Founding of the Royal Society*
   $\frac{1}{2}$" VHS   24 min.
   Describes the various scientific groups that began to form in 17th-century England: at Gresham College, London, in 1645 and Oxford, 1657, culminating in the founding of the British Royal Society in 1660. Looks at the problems addressed by the Society, particularly the calculation of longitude at sea, which led to the founding of the Royal Greenwich Observatory. Ends with a discussion of Newton's *Principia Mathematica*, 1687.
   The Open University   1988
   Md G

9. *Galileo: The Challenge of Reason*
16 mm film ½" VHS   26 min.
Dramatizes the individual vs. establishment conflict between Galileo and the authorities of the day. Focuses on Galileo's censure by the Roman Catholic Inquisition due to his expounding of scientific theories that contradicted faith-supported doctrines.
Western Civilization: Majesty and Madness series   1969
IU; O Kent U

10. *Galileo and His Universe*
16 mm film   22 min.
In 1616 Galileo Galilei's discoveries, inventions, and theories about the solar system have placed him in direct conflict with the established views of the time. News correspondents conduct on-the-spot interviews with principal figures in the controversy, including noted astronomer Johannes Kepler.
CBS: You Are There series   1971
Co U; IU

11. *Golden Section*
16 mm film   15 min.
Using animation over photography, the proportional relation of the historical ratio used in art, mathematics, and architecture is described. The golden mean's appearance in flowers, trees, and geometry is shown, and the Fibonacci sequence is discussed.
Fleetwood Films   1968
O Kent U; N Sy U

12. *The Great Art—Solving Equations*
16 mm film   25 min.
Discusses the solution of cubic equations in Italy in the 16th century. Traces the origin of European algebra and comments on the work of Pacioli, Scipione del Ferro, and Cardano and Tartaglia's methods for solving cubic equations.
The Open University   1974
IU; O Kent U

13. *The Idea of Numbers: An Introduction to Number Systems*
16 mm film   14 min.
The history of counting and accounting is told, from stones, sticks, and notches to the binary number system: Babylonian, Asian, Mayan, Arabian, and medieval systems are considered.
Visual Education Inc.   1971
IU; Ct U

14. *Islamic Knowledge*
½" VHS   30 min.
Highlights the contributions of Islam to modern science and technology, including its system of calculation, its symbols for numbers, and its concepts of astronomy, physics, medicine, and engineering.
World of Islam series   1983
P.S.U.

15. *The Liberation of Algebra*
    $\frac{1}{2}$" VHS   25 min.
    Filmed in Ireland, this tape examines the work of William Rowan Hamilton in Dublin and George Boole in Cork. From Hamilton's discovery of quaternions to Boole's *The Laws of Thought*, the effects of these concepts are traced to astrophysics and computer design.
    The Open University   1988
    P.S.U.

16. *The Life and Times of Bertrand Russell*
    16 mm film   80 min.
    Presents an autobiographical interview with British mathematician and philosopher Bertrand Russell. Includes statements from a number of noted personalities, newsreel footage, and filming around Russell's home.
    BBC   1967
    IU

17. *Luca Pacioli: Unsung Hero of the Renaissance*
    $\frac{1}{2}$" VHS   25 min.
    Discusses the life and work of Luca Pacioli, the Father of Accounting. Pacioli's work and career in mathematics and teaching are reviewed. His authorship of the *Summa* is highlighted, as well as his association with Leonardo da Vinci. This tape provides a good survey of the mood of mathematics during the Renaissance.
    Southwestern Publishing Co.   1990

18. *Majestic Clockwork*
    $\frac{1}{2}$" VHS   52 min.
    Describes Albert Einstein's work on the general theory of relativity. Explains some of the features of this theory and stresses the social responsibility of science.
    BBC: Ascent of Man series, #7   1974
    P.S.U.

19. *The Man Who Loved Numbers*
    $\frac{1}{2}$" VHS   57 min.
    Profiles the life and work of Srinivasa Ramanujan, the brilliant self-taught mathematician from southern India who was invited by G. H. Hardy of Trinity College to continue his work in England. In 1920 at age 33 Ramanujan died, leaving behind notebooks full of work that is still being studied.
    WGBH, Nova series   1988
    P.S.U.

20. *Mathematical Mystery Tour*
    $\frac{1}{2}$" VHS   57 min.
    A look at the world of pure mathematics conducted by eminent mathematicians. Considers proofs with numbers greater than infinity and on theorems proving that some statements can never be proved. Explains why proofs done in 300 B.C. are still considered perfect, and discusses the impact of computers on abstract mathematics.
    WGBH: Nova series   1985
    P.S.U.

21. *Mathematics of the Honeycomb*
    16 mm film   13 min.
    The elegance of the honeycomb, admired by the Greek mathematician Pappus, was not fully appreciated until modern mathematical methods were applied. Through a historical and analytical approach to the honeycomb problem, the viewer is led to appreciate the importance of mathematics in science and engineering.
    Moody Institute of Science   1977
    IU

22. *Music of the Spheres*
    16 mm film $\frac{1}{2}$" VHS   51 min.
    Traces the evolution of mathematics and explores the relationship of numbers to musical harmony, early astronomy, and perspective in painting. Follows the spread of Greek ideas through the courts and bazaars of the Islamic empire to Renaissance Europe.
    BBC: Ascent of Man series, #5   1974
    IU

23. *Mystery of Stonehenge*
    16 mm film $\frac{1}{2}$" VHS   57 min.
    Explains and tests the premise of Gerald Hawkins that Stonehenge, the huge stone circle in England, was built as an astronomical computer by early humans.
    CBS   1965
    P.S.U.

24. *Newton: The Mind That Found the Future*
    16 mm film $\frac{1}{2}$" VHS   21 min.
    Dramatizes some events in the career of Sir Isaac Newton, concentrating on his discovery of the laws of universal gravity. Points out Newton's employment of the scientific method and lists his other contributions, specifically differential calculus, the revolving telescope, and work in the areas of light and optics.
    Western Civilization: Majesty and Madness series   1970
    IU; O Kent U

25. *New Worlds from Old*
    16 mm film   25 min.
    Traces the history of investigation into Euclid's parallel postulate during the 18th and 19th centuries. Discusses the strategy of Saccheri, examines geometric theorems, and explains the significance of Einstein's general theory of relativity, which has led to mathematicians' acceptance of a non-Euclidean universe.
    The Open University   1975
    IU; O Kent U

26. *Numbers Now and Then*
    16 mm film   25 min.
    Traces the history of our number system from the Sumerians, Babylonians, Egyptians, Greeks, and Hindu-Arabic numerals. Discusses place value, decimal systems, simple calculations, and algebraic equations.
    The Open University   1974
    IU; O Kent U

27. *Paris and the New Mathematics*
    $\frac{1}{2}$" VHS   25 min.
    Centering on the life of one of France's greatest revolutionary mathematicians, Gaspard Monge, this presentation shows how he founded the École Polytechnique, originally to train military engineers. It was at this school that the postrevolutionary mathematicians trained and did their research.
    The Open University   1988
    Md G

28. *Points of View: Perspective and Projection*
    16 mm film   25 min.
    Discusses the evolution of perspective in Renaissance art. Introduces the mathematical ideas underlying the principle of projection and section. Explains the theorems of projective geometry developed by Desargues and Pascal in the 17th century.
    The Open University   1975
    IU; O Kent U

29. *Quaternions: A Herald of Modern Algebra*
    16 mm film   24 min.
    Presents the life and work of William Hamilton, whose thoughts produced noncommutative algebra. Master of nine ancient languages by age ten, he became interested in Euclid. For fifteen years he worked on the problem of generalizing complex numbers to three dimensions. When he found a solution and realized that it led to four-dimensional space, he coined the term *quaternion*.
    The Open University   1975
    IU

30. *Root Two: Geometry or Arithmetic*
    16 mm film   25 min.
    Discusses the line as a unit of measurement and questions how incommensurable magnitudes were handled before the discovery of the proportion theory found in Euclid's *Elements*. Traces evidence in theories arrived at by the Greeks, the Pythagoreans, Plato, and others in order to describe the foundation–crisis interpretation.
    The Open University   1974
    IU; O Kent U

31. *Royal Road*
    16 mm film $\frac{1}{2}$" VHS   28 min.
    Retraces the logic of Einstein to demonstrate that space and time are curved or warped by the distribution of matter in the universe, and that matter and energy move along this curvature of space/time. Four-dimensional geometry is shown to be a cornerstone of the general theory of relativity.
    BBC: Understanding Space and Time series   1980
    CU

32. *Time for Change–The Calculus*
    16 mm film   25 min.
    Considers the early history of the calculus in Renaissance times. Examines the method of indivisibles, the area under a cycloidal arch, Fermat's tangent method and his calculation of areas, Huygens' study of the swing of a pendulum, and the rectification of the

semicubical parabola.
The Open University   1974
O Kent U

33. *The Vernacular Tradition*
$\frac{1}{2}$" VHS   25 min.
Explains that vernacular works of the Renaissance were those concerned with mathematical calculations to solve practical problems. Traces algebraic and numerical problem-solving back to Arabic, Hindu, and European influences in the 15th and 16th centuries.
The Open University   1986
P.S.U.

Sources

CU
University of California
Extension Media Center
2176 Shattuck Avenue
Berkeley, CA 94704
415-642-0460

Co U
University of Colorado
Academic Services
Box 378
Boulder, CO 80309-0379
303-492-7341

Ct U
University of Connecticut
Center for Instructional
    Media & Technology
249 Glenbrook Road
Storrs, CT 06269-2001
203-486-2530

IU
University of Illinois
University Film Center
1325 South Oak Street
Champaign, IL 61820
800-367-3458

Md G
Media Guild
11722 Sorrento Valley Road
San Diego, CA 92121-1021
619-755-9191

N Sy U
Syracuse University
Film Rental Center
1455 E. Colvin Street
Syracuse, NY 13210
800-223-2409

O Kent U
Kent State University
Audio Visual Services
330 University Library
Kent, OH 44242
800-338-5718

P.S.U.
The Pennsylvania State University
Audio Visual Services
Special Services Building
University Park, PA 16802
800-826-0132

Southwestern Publishing Co.
5101 Madison Road
Cincinnati, OH 45227
800-543-0487

WU
University of Wisconsin–Madison
Bureau of Audio Visual Instruction
1327 University Avenue
P.O. Box 2093
Madison, WI 53701-2983
608-262-3902

An Interesting Project

Many countries issue postage stamps that depict historical mathematical events and/or personages. Colorful and informative displays can be devised using such stamps. Student collectors can share the fruits of their hobby while promoting an interest in the history of mathematics.

CHAPTER 7

Where to From Here?

Throughout this book we have discussed strategies for using the history of mathematics as part of the teaching of mathematics. We have introduced and developed a variety of specific strategies, such as using posters, reports, activities, and films. You can strengthen and expand any or all of these teaching ideas. You could, for example, devise more activities and increase your collection of historical problems. The history of mathematics is certainly a rich and accommodating field from which to obtain resources. It is my hope that now that you have been better introduced to some methods of developing and using a historical perspective in your teaching, you will go on to develop a personal collection of historical teaching ideas and resources.

In reading this book, trying the suggested strategies, and using the included materials, you should have learned something more about the history of mathematics itself. We hope this learning will be contagious. I know that in my own case, as I increase my historical knowledge, I also increase my historical and mathematical curiosity and constantly find new questions for which I must seek answers. As we strengthen our own knowledge about the history of mathematics, we are better able to reflect it in our teaching. Thus, perhaps the best means of insuring and maintaining a historical teaching perspective is to study the history of mathematics.

For teachers who have had formal studies in the history of mathematics, perhaps as part of their teacher-training program, a background on which to build already exists. Others of us (myself included) must obtain our historical knowledge through personal readings, in-service workshops, and professional conferences. State and regional mathematics associations and, of course, the National Council of Teachers of Mathematics (NCTM) usually have presentations and even short workshops on the history of mathematics at their annual meetings. Even teachers knowledgeable in the history of mathematics can benefit from attendance at these events as they provide a continuous source of new ideas and information on the subject. Meeting other teachers and exchanging views on using the history of mathematics and available resources provides an optimum means of learning about the history of mathematics.

A good variety of materials exists for self-study, but the selection and use of specific materials depends on their availability and the personal capacity and needs of the learner. From experience, I would suggest a gradual exposure to the history of mathematics. Read some general survey materials and begin to understand the trends in the history of mathematics, the significant events, and important people. Obtain a feel for the larger picture and then select the specific concepts and events that personally interest you as a teacher and would be useful in your teaching. Later you could do more concentrated readings on these topics. For example, if you are a teacher of Algebra I, you might not be interested in the development of differential equations but would like to know something about the historical solution processes for linear equations. You should then seek out information on the history and solution of simple equations.

My collection of readings, *From Five Fingers to Infinity* (1994), is designed to provide a historical survey of primary mathematical concepts and is intended principally for the use of teachers. Other popular surveys are provided by: Michael Moffatt et al., *The Ages of Mathematics*, 4 vols. (1977); Edna Kramer, *The Main Stream of Mathematics* (1988); and D. J. Struik, *A Concise History of Mathematics* (1987). More comprehensive surveys are supplied by Howard Eves, *An Introduction to the History of Mathematics* (1990) and David Burton, *The History of Mathematics: An Introduction* (1991). These latter two books are intended as texts for university courses; both contain an excellent variety of exercises that can also be used at the secondary level. A less comprehensive but most valuable survey book for a teacher is the NCTM's *Historical Topics for the Mathematics Classroom* (revised 1989). Also recommended for readings of an introductory nature would be Lancelot Hogben's *The Wonderful World of Mathematics* (1968) and the more recent work of Douglas Campbell and John Higgins, *Mathematics: People, Problems, Results* (1984).

For those readers who would like to delve into materials from original sources, several excellent compilations exist. Three such collections easily come to mind: Henrietta Midonick, *The Treasury of Mathematics: A Collection of Source Material* (1965); John Fauvel and Jeremy Gray, *The History of Mathematics: A Reader* (1989); and Ronald Calinger, *Classics of Mathematics* (1982). For still others who might like an interpretation of the history of mathematics, the works of Morris Kline are appealing, especially his *Mathematics: A Cultural Approach* (1962).

Teachers' journals and periodicals occasionally carry articles on the history of mathematics and its use in teaching. A listing of these is provided in C. B. Read's article in *School Science and Mathematics* (1976). Currently, the most fruitful sources of such articles are *The Mathematics Teacher*, *School Science and Mathematics*, and *Consortium: The Newsletter of the Consortium for Mathematics and Its Applications* (COMAP). References to more specialized sources of information on the history of mathematics are given in the bibliography at the end of this book.

Teacher involvement with the history of mathematics is self-enriching in the sense that in instituting the teaching strategies discussed above we, as teachers, obtain further opportunities for our learning. In carrying out a historical project with a class or viewing a film on the history of mathematics, we learn more about that history. Student projects and reports will supply interesting details and perhaps raise further historical questions that can be investigated. The history of mathematics is both an open and a tantalizing subject—you never learn enough about it and, usually, the more you learn about it, the more you want to learn about it.

A Selected Bibliography

This bibliography is offered for those readers who may wish to extend and strengthen their knowledge of the history of mathematics. The selection of materials is based on availability of items and general usefulness and is certainly not intended to be comprehensive. Throughout this listing, the following coding system is used in brackets to call attention to particular features of certain works:

[A] Supplies ideas for activities.

[L] Appropriate for high school library acquisition.

[P] A good source of problems.

[S] Especially valuable for self-study.

1. Periodicals

The following periodicals are specifically written for mathematics educators, and their contents occasionally include features devoted to the history of mathematics and its uses:

Consortium: The Newsletter of the Consortium for Mathematics and Its Applications. Published quarterly by COMAP, Inc., 60 Lowell Street, Arlington, MA 02174-4131.

The Mathematics Teacher. Published monthly, September through May, by the National Council of Teachers of Mathematics [NCTM], 1906 Association Drive, Reston, VA 22091.

School Science and Mathematics. Published monthly, October through May, 126 Life Sciences Bldg., Bowling Green State University, Bowling Green, OH 43403.

In seeking out articles prior to 1976, the following reference is especially helpful:

Read, C. B. "Articles on the History of Mathematics: A Bibliography of Articles Appearing in Six Periodicals," *School Science and Mathematics* 59 (1959): 689–717; updated in 1976 with J. K. Bidwell, 76 (1976): 477–483, 581–598, 687–703.

2. Resources for Using the History of Mathematics in Teaching

Mitchell, Merle. *Mathematical History: Activities, Puzzles, Stories, and Games*. Reston, VA: NCTM, 1978.   [A]

National Council of Teachers of Mathematics. *Historical Topics for the Mathematics Classroom*, 2nd ed. Reston, VA: NCTM, 1989.   [A]

Pappas, Theoni. *Mathematics Appreciation*. San Carlo, CA: Math Aids, 1986.   [A]

Popp, Walter. *History of Mathematics: Topics for Schools*. London: Open University Press, 1978.

3. Books on the History of Numbers

Dantzig, Tobias. *Number: the Language of Science*, 4th rev. ed. New York: Free Press-Macmillan, 1967.

Freitag, H.T. and A. H. Freitag *The Number Story*. Reston, VA: NCTM, 1960.

Ifrah, Georges. *From One to Zero: A Universal History of Numbers*. New York: Viking Penguin, 1985.

Menninger, Karl. *Number Words and Number Symbols: A Cultural History of Numbers*. Cambridge MA: MIT Press, 1977.

Smeltzer Donald. *Man and Number*. New York: Collier Books, 1962.

Smith D. E., and J. Ginsburg. *Numbers and Numerals*. Reston, VA: NCTM, 1958.

4. General Survey Books

Boyer, Carl B., and Uta Merzbach. *A History of Mathematics*, 2nd ed. New York: John Wiley & Sons, 1991.

Burton, David M. *The History of Mathematics: An Introduction*, 2nd ed. Dubuque, IA: William C. Brown, 1991.   [P]

Cajori, F. *A History of Mathematics*. New York: Chelsea, 1985.

Eves, Howard. *An Introduction to the History of Mathematics*, 6th ed. Philadelphia: Saunders, College Publishing, 1990.   [P, S]

Gittleman, Arthur. *History of Mathematics.* Columbus, OH: Charles E. Merrill Publishing Co., 1975.

Katz, Victor. *A History of Mathematics: An Introduction.* New York: Harper Collins, 1993.

Kline, Morris. *Mathematical Thought from Ancient to Modern Times,* 3 vols. New York: Oxford University Press, 1972.

Scott, J. F. *A History of Mathematics: From Antiquity to the Beginning of the Nineteenth Century.* New York: Barnes & Noble, 1969.

Struik, D. J. *A Concise History of Mathematics.* New York: Dover Publications, 1987.   [P]

Swetz, Frank. *From Five Fingers to Infinity: A Journey Through the History of Mathematics.* Peru, IL: Open Court, 1994.   [S]

5. Selective and Interpretive Works

Aaboe, Asger. *Episodes from the Early History of Mathematics.* Washington, DC: Mathematical Association of America, 1978.   [L]

Baron, M. E. *The Origins of the Infinitesimal Calculus.* New York: Dover Publications, 1987.

Bell, E. T. *Men of Mathematics.* New York: Simon and Schuster, 1965.

Bergamini, David. *Mathematics*–Alexandria, VA: Time–Life Books, 1970.

Berggren, J. L. *Episodes in the Mathematics of Medieval Islam.* New York: Springer–Verlag, 1986.

Boyer, Carl B. *The History of the Calculus and Its Conceptual Development.* New York: Dover Publications, 1959.

Bunt, L. N. H., P. S. Jones, and J. D. Bedient, *The Historical Roots of Elementary Mathematics.* Englewood, NJ: Prentice–Hall, 1976.

Calinger, Ronald, ed. *Classics of Mathematics*, Oak Park, IL: Moore Publishing Co., 1982.

Campbell, Douglas M., and John Higgins. *Mathematics: People, Problems, Results,* 3 vols. Belmont, CA: Wadsworth, 1984.   [L, S]

Chace, A. B. *The Rhind Mathematical Papyrus* (reprint). Reston, VA: NCTM, 1979.

Davis, P., and R. Hersh. *The Mathematical Experience*. Boston: Berkhaüser, 1981.

Dilke, O. A. W. *Mathematics and Measurement*. Berkeley, CA : University of California Press, 1987.

Dörrie, H. *100 Great Problems of Elementary Mathematics: Their History and Solution*. New York: Dover Publications, 1965.   [P]

Dunham, William. *Journey Through Genius: The Great Theorems of Mathematics*. New York: John Wiley & Sons, 1990.   [A]

Eves, Howard. *Great Moments in Mathematics (After 1650)*. Washington, DC: The Mathematical Association of America, 1982.   [S]

_____ . *Great Moments in Mathematics (Before 1650)*. Washington, DC: The Mathematical Association of America, 1981.   [S]

_____ . *In Mathematical Circles*, 2 vols. Boston: Prindle, Weber & Schmidt, 1969.

_____ . *Mathematical Circles Adieu*. Boston: Prindle, Weber & Schmidt, 1977.

_____ . *Mathematical Circles Revisited*. Boston: Prindle, Weber & Schmidt, 1971.

_____ . *Mathematical Circles Squared*. Boston: Prindle, Weber & Schmidt, 1972.

_____ . *Return to Mathematical Circles*. Boston: Prindle, Weber, Schmidt & Kent, 1988.

Gillings, Richards J. *Mathematics in the Time of the Pharaohs*. New York: Dover Publications, 1982.

Hofstadter, D. *Gödel, Escher, and Bach: An Eternal Golden Braid*. New York: Vintage Books, 1979.

Hogbe, Lancelot. *Mathematics for the Millions*. London: Merlin, 1989.   [L]

_____ . *The Wonderful World of Mathematics*. New York: Doubleday and Company, 1968.

Hooper, Alfred. *Makers of Mathematics*. New York: Vintage Books, 1948.

Joseph, George G. *The Crest of the Peacock: Non-European Roots of Mathematics*. New York: St. Martin Press, 1991.

Karpinski, L. *The History of Arithmetic*. Chicago: Rand McNally, 1925.

Kline, Morris. *Mathematics: A Cultural Approach*. Reading, MA: Addison–Wesley, 1962.   [S]

_____ . *Mathematics: The Loss of Certainty*. New York: Oxford University Press, 1983.

_____ . *Mathematics in Western Culture*. New York: Oxford University Press, 1953.

_____ . *Mathematics: An Introduction to Its Spirit and Use*. San Francisco: W. H. Freeman and Co., 1979.

_____ ed. *Mathematics in the Modern World*. San Francisco: W. H. Freeman and Co., 1968.

Kramer, Edna E. *The Main Stream of Mathematics*. Princeton Junction, NJ: Scholars Bookshelf, 1988.   [L, S]

_____ . *The Nature and Growth of Modern Mathematics*. New York: Hawthorn, 1970.   [L]

Li Yan and Du Shiran. *Chinese Mathematics: A Concise History*. New York: Oxford University Press, 1987.

Loomis, Elisha. *The Pythagorean Proposition* (reprint). Reston, VA: NCTM, 1968.   [A]

Meschkowski, H. *Ways of Thought of Great Mathematics*. San Francisco: Holden–Day, 1964.

Midonick, H. O., ed. *The Treasury of Mathematics*. New York: Philosophical Library, 1965.

Moffatt, Michael, ed. *The Ages of Mathematics*, 4 vols. New York: Doubleday, 1977.   [S]

Neugebauer, Otto. *The Exact Sciences in Antiquity*. New York: Dover Publications, 1969.

Resnikoff, H. L., and R. O. Wells. *Mathematics in Civilization*. New York: Dover Publications, 1985.   [S]

Smith, David E. *History of Mathematics*, 2 vols. New York: Dover Publications, 1958.

Swetz, Frank. *Capitalism and Arithmetic: The New Math of the 15th Century*. Peru, IL: Open Court, 1987.   [P, L]

_____ , and T. I. Kao. *Was Pythagoras Chinese? An Examination of Right Triangle Theory in Ancient China*. University Park, PA: The Pennsylvania State University Press, 1977.   [A]

Waerden, B. L. van der. *Geometry and Algebra in Ancient Civilizations*. New York: Springer–Verlag, 1983.

Wills, Herbert. *Leonardo's Dessert: No Pi*. Reston, VA: NCTM, 1985.

Zeintarn, M. *The History of Computing*. Framingham, MA: C.W. Communications, 1981.

6. Biographical References

Adamczeivski, Jan. *Nicolaus Copernicus and His Epoch*. Philadelphia: Copernicus Society of America, 1973.

Albers, Donald, and G. L. Alexanderson, eds. *Courant in Göttingen and New York*. New York: Springer–Verlag, 1976.

Bell, Eric T. *Men of Mathematics*. New York: Simon & Schuster, 1986.

Bishop, Morris. *Pascal: The Life of a Genius*. New York: Reynal & Hitchcock, 1936.

Bühler, W. K. *Gauss: A Biographical Study*. New York: Springer–Verlag, 1981.

Coolidge, J. L. *The Mathematics of Great Amateurs*. New York: Oxford University Press, 1949.

Dedron P., and J. Itard. *Mathematics and Mathematicians*, 2 vols. London: Transworld Publications, 1973.

Dijksterhuis, E. J. *Archimedes*. New York: Humanities Press, 1957.

Drake, Stillman. *Galileo at Work: His Scientific Biography*. Chicago: University of Chicago Press, 1978.

Dunnington, G. W. *Carl Friedrich Gauss: Titan of Science*. New York: Hafner, 1955.

Flegg, Graham, et al. *Nicolas Chuquet: Renaissance Mathematician.* Boston: D. Redel Publishing Co., 1985.

Gies, Joseph and Francis Gies. *Leonardo of Pisa and the New Mathematics of the Middle Ages.* New York: Thomas Y. Crowell Co., 1969.

Gillispie, C. C, ed. *Dictionary of Scientific Biography,* 16 vols. New York: Charles Scribner's Sons, 1970–80.

Haldane, Elizabeth. *Descartes: His Life and Times.* New York: American Scholar Publications, 1966.

Hall, Tord. *Carl Friedrich Gauss.* Cambridge, MA: M.I.T. Press, 1970.

Hankins, Thomas L. *Jean d'Alembert: Science and the Enlightenment.* Oxford: Clarendon Press, 1970.

Hart, Ivor. *Makers of Science: Mathematics, Physics, and Astronomy.* Freeport, NY: Books for Libraries Press, 1968.

Heims, Steve. *John Von Neumann and Norbert Wiener.* Cambridge, MA: M.I.T. Press, 1980.

Herivel, J. *Joseph Fourier, the Man and the Physicist.* Oxford: Clarendon Press, 1975.

Hodgers, Andrew. *Alan Turing: The Enigma.* New York: Simon & Schuster, 1983.

Hooper, Alfred. *Makers of Mathematics.* New York: Random House, 1948.

Hyman, Anthony. *Charles Babbage, Pioneer of the Computer.* Princeton, NJ: Princeton University Press, 1982.

Infeld, Leopold. *Albert Einstein: His Work and Its Influence on Our Lives.* New York: Charles Scribner's Sons, 1950.

_____ . *Whom the Gods Love: The Story of Evariste Galois.* New York, McGraw–Hill, 1948.

Koestler, Arthur. *The Watershed: A Life of Kepler.* New York: Doubleday, 1960.

Lamb, Harold. *Omar Khayyám: A Life.* New York: Doubleday, 1936.

Mahoney, Michael. *The Mathematical Career of Pierre de Fermat (1601–1655).* Princeton, NJ: Princeton University Press, 1973.

Manuel, Frank. *A Portrait of Isaac Newton*. Cambridge, MA: Harvard University Press, 1968.

McMullin, Ernan, ed. *Galileo: Man of Science*. New York: Basic Books, 1967.

Merz, John. *Leibniz*. New York: Hacker Press, 1948.

Meschkowski, Herbert. *The Ways of Thought of Great Mathematicians*. San Francisco: Holde–Day, 1964.

Mesmard, Jean. *Pascal: His Life and Works*. New York: Philosophical Library, 1952.

Moore, Louis Trenchard. *Isaac Newton: A Biography*. New York: Charles Scribner's Sons, 1962.

Muir, Jane. *Of Men and Numbers*. New York: Dodd Mead, 1961.

Ore, Oystein. *Cardano, the Gambling Scholar*. Princeton, NJ: Princeton University Press, 1953.

_____ . *Neils Henrik Abel, Mathematician Extraordinary*. Minneapolis, MN: University of Minnesota Press, 1957.

Pólya, George. *The Pólya Picture Album: Encounters of a Mathematician*. (G. L. Alexanderson, ed.). Boston: Birkhäuser, 1957.

Reid, George. *Courant in Göttingen and New York: The Story of an Improbable Mathematician*. New York: Springer–Verlag, 1976.

_____ . *Hilbert*. New York: Springer–Verlag, 1970.

Sarton, George. *Six Wings: Men of Science in the Renaissance*. Bloomington, IN: Indiana University Press, 1957.

Schaaf, William. *Carl Friedrich Gauss: Prince of Mathematics*. New York: Franklin Watts, 1964.

Taylor, E. G. R. *The Mathematical Practitioners of Tudor and Stuart England*. Cambridge: The University Press, 1954.

Taylor, R. Emmett. *No Royal Road: Luca Pacioli and His Times*. Chapel Hill, NC: University of North Carolina Press, 1942.

Turnbull, H. W. *The Great Mathematicians*. New York: New York University Press, 1961.

Vrooman, J. R. *René Descartes: A Biography*. New York: Putnam, 1970.

Young, Lawrence. *Mathematicians and Their Times*. Amsterdam, Holland: North–Holland, 1981.

7. Women in Mathematics

Alic, Margaret. *Hypatia's Heritage: The History of Women in Science from Antiquity to the End of the Nineteenth Century*. New York: The Women's Press, 1986.

Baum, Joan. *The Calculating Passion of Ada Byron*. Hamden, CT : Archeon Books, 1986.

Brewer, James, and Martha Smith. *Emmy Noether: A Tribute to Her Life and Work*. New York: Marcel Dekken, 1981.

Dick, Auguste. *Emmy Noether, 1882–1935*. Basel, Switzerland: Birkhäuser Verlag, 1970.

Ehrman, Ester. *Mme. du Châtelet: Scientist, Philosopher, and Feminist of the Enlightenment*. Leamington Spa, U.K.: Berg, 1986.

Grinstein, Louise, and Paul Campbell. *Women of Mathematics: A Biobibliographic Sourcebook*. Westport, CT: Greenwood Press, 1987.

Kennedy, Donald. *Little Sparrow: A Portrait of Sophie Kovalesky*. Athens, OH: Ohio University Press, 1983.

Koblitz, Ann Hibner. *A Convergence of Lives—Sofia Kovalevskaia: Scientist, Writer, Revolutionary*. Boston: Birkhäuser, 1985.

Moore, Doris Langley. *Ada, Countess of Lovelace: Byron's Legitimate Daughter*. London: John Murray, 1977.

Osen, Lynn. *Women in Mathematics*. Cambridge MA: M.I.T. Press, 1974.

Perl, Teri. *Math Equals: Biographies of Women Mathematicians & Related Activities*. Reading, MA: Addison Wesley, 1978.

8. Special Topics [A]

A. Magic Squares

Andrews, William S. *Magic Squares and Cubes*. New York: Dover Publications, 1960.

Aviv, Cherie A., and Sid Rachlin. "Magic Cubes: A Total Experience." *Mathematics Teacher* 74 (September 1981): 464–72.

Benson, Williams, and Oswald Jacoby. *New Recreations with Magic Squares*. New York: Dover Publications, 1976.

Bernard, John. "Constructing Magic Square Number Games." *Arithmetic Teacher* 26 (October 1978): 36–38.

Bright, George W. "Ideas." *Arithmetic Teacher* 25 (October 1977): 30–34.

Cohen Martin P., and John Bernard. "From Magic Squares to Vector Spaces." *Mathematics Teacher* 64 (January 1982): 76–77, 64.

El-Zaidi, S. M. "Reader Reflections: Constructing Magic Squares." *Mathematics Teacher* 75 (November 1982): 637.

Enge, Roger. "Reader Reflections: Magic-Square Designs." *Mathematics Teacher* 77 (November 1984): 596

Engelmeyer, William J. "Magic Squares." *Mathematics Teacher* 68 (May 1975): 399–402

Freitag, Herta, and Arthur H. Freitag "The Magic of a Square." *Mathematics Teacher* 63 (January 1970): 5–14.

Gardner, Martin. "A Magic Square." *Mathematics Teacher* 61 (January 1968): 18.

Gilmore, Hal. "Sharing Teaching Ideas: Checking with Magic Squares." *Mathematics Teacher* 77 (May 1984): 351–52.

Gorts, Jeannie. "Magic Square Patterns." *Arithmetic Teacher* 16 (April 1969): 314–16.

Hough, Herbert W. "Reader Reflections: Magic Squares as Vectors." *Mathematics Teacher* 75 (December 1982): 734–35.

Kenney, Margaret J. "An Artful Application Using Magic Squares." *Mathematics Teacher* 75 (January 1982): 83–89.

Lott, Johnny W. "Behold a Magic Square." *Arithmetic Teacher* 24 (March 1977): 228–29.

Lyon, Betty Clayton. "Using Magic Borders to Generate Magic Squares." *Mathematics Teacher* 77 (March 1984): 223–26.

Maletsky, Evan M. "Manipulating Magic Squares." *Mathematics Teacher* 65 (December 1972): 729–32.

Munger, Ralph. "An Algebraic Treatment of Magic Squares." *Mathematics Teacher* 66 (February 1973): 101–07.

Nemecek, Paul M. "Bicentennial Magic Square." *Mathematics Teacher* 69 (November 1976): 545.

O'Sullivan, Ellen P. "Magic Squares for Average Learners Too." *Arithmetic Teacher* 23 (October 1976) : 427–28.

Pagni, David L. "Magic Squares: Would You Believe . . .?" *Arithmetic Teacher* 21 (May 1974): 439–41.

Reiter, Harold B. "Problem Solving with Magic Rectangles." *Mathematics Teacher* 79 (April 1986): 242–45.

Sawada, Daiyo. "Magic Squares: Extensions into Mathematics." *Arithmetic Teacher* 21 (March 1974): 183–88.

Swetz, Frank. "Mysticism and Magic in the Number Squares of Old China." *Mathematics Teacher* 71 (January 1978): 50–56.

Van Engen, Henry. "A Note on 'An Algebraic Treatment of Magic Squares.' " *Mathematics Teacher* 66 (December 1973): 747.

Williams, Horace E. "A Note on Magic Squares." *Mathematics Teacher* 67 (October 1974) : 511–513.

B. Pythagorean Triples

Archambeau, Sr. Mary Leona. "Pythagorean Triples Grouped into Families." *Mathematics Teacher* 62 (March 1968): 251–252.

Arpaia, Pasquale J. "Discoveries in Mathematics." *Mathematics Teacher* 65 (May 1972): 463–65.

Brown, Susan A. "A Surprising Fact About Pythagorean Triples." *Mathematics Teacher* 78 (October 1985): 540–41.

Cohen, Israel. "Pythagorean Numbers." *Mathematics Teacher* 67 (November 1974): 667–69

DiDomenico, Angelo S. "Eureka! Pythagorean Triples from the Addition Table." *Mathematics Teacher* 78 (May 1985): 336–38.

Gillman, Leonard. "Reader Reflections: Pythagorean Serendipity II." *Mathematics Teacher* 74 (November 1981): 675.

Hills, Michael S. "Reader Reflections: Isosceles Pythagorean Triangles." *Mathematics Teacher* 76 (December 1983): 648–49.

Jones, Alan B. "Reader Reflections: Pythagorean Serendipity III." *Mathematics Teacher* 74 (December 1981): 681.

Marche, M. M. "Sharing Teaching Ideas: A Pythagorean Curiosity." *Mathematics Teacher* 77 (November 1984): 611–13.

Moore, Charles G. "Rectangle Triples." *Mathematics Teacher* 76 (January 1983): 58–59.

Ness, Harold M., Jr. "Reader Reflections: A Lesson with Pythagorean Triples." *Mathematics Teacher* 74 (May 1981): 388.

_____ . "Reader Reflections: Pythagorean Triples." *Mathematics Teacher* 74 (February 1981): 88.

Roensch, Steve. "Reader Reflections: Pythagorean Triples." *Mathematics Teacher* 70 (May 1977): 388–89.

Rothbart, Andre, and Bruce Paulsell. "Pythagorean Triples: A New, Easy-to-Derive Formula with Some Geometric Applications." *Mathematics Teacher* 67 (March 1974): 215–18.

Ryden, Robert. "Nearly Isosceles Pythagorean Triples." *Mathematics Teacher* 76 (January 1983): 52–56.

Sastry, K. R. S. "Reader Reflections: Is Pythagoras Nasty?" *Mathematics Teacher* 78 (May 1985): 332–33.

Simmons, Jo Ann. "Reader Reflections: Pythagorean Serendipity." *Mathematics Teacher* 74 (January 1981): 10.

Smith, Ronald E. "Reader Reflections: Pythagorean Triples/Near Triples." *Mathematics Teacher* 76 (December 1983): 649.

Spaulding, Raymond E. "Pythagorean Puzzles." *Mathematics Teacher* 67 (February 1974): 143–46.

Szczepanski, Ronald. "Sharing Teaching Ideas: Generating Primitive Pythagorean Triples—A Computer Solution." *Mathematics Teacher* 77 (March 1984): 191–92.

Ugochukwu, Uko. "Reader Reflections: Pythagorean Serendipity IV." *Mathematics Teacher* 76 (January 1983): 63.

Waters, William M., Jr. "Notes on an Extension of Pythagorean Triples in Arithmetic Progression." *Mathematics Teacher* 62 (December 1969): 633–35.

Watson, James D. "Pythagorean Triples: What Kind? How Many?" *Mathematics Teacher* 69 (February 1976): 108–110.

Wolodiger, Fred, Carol Bourdette, J. Orten Gadd, and Robert W. Prielipp. "Reader Reflections: Triples." *Mathematics Teacher* 69 (November 1976): 537–39.

Wong, Ngai-ying. "Reader Reflections: Nearly Triples." *Mathematics Teacher* 76 (November 1983): 563.

C. Polygonal and Figurate Numbers

Colman, Weaver. "Figurate Numbers." *Mathematics Teacher* 67 (November 1974): 661–666.

Hamberg, Charles L., and Thomas M. Green. "An Application of Triangular Numbers to Counting." *Mathematics Teacher* (April 1967): 339–342.

Hartman, Janet. "Figurate Numbers." *Mathematics Teacher* 60 (January 1976): 47–50.

Harvey, Margaret A., and Bonnie H. Litwiller. "Polygonal Numbers : A Study of Patterns." *Arithmetic Teacher* 17 (January 1970): 33–38.

Mauland, Lyle E. "An Exercise with Polygonal Numbers." *Mathematics Teacher* 78 (May 1985): 340–344.

Miller, Janice, and F. Max Stein. "A Generalization of Triangular Numbers." *Mathematics Teacher* 56 (October 1963): 414–418.

Miller, William. "Polygonal Numbers and Recursion." *Mathematics Teacher* 85 (October 1990): 555–562.

Olson, Melfried, Gerald K. Goff, and Murray Blose. "Triangular Numbers: The Building Block of Figurate Numbers." *Mathematics Teacher* 76 (November 1983): 624–625.

Ouellette, Hugh. "Discovery with Number Triangles." *Mathematics Teacher* 71 (November 1978): 678–682.

_____ . "Number Triangles—A Discovery Lesson." *Mathematics Teacher* 68 (December 1975): 671–674.

Pinkerton, Kenny. "Triangular Differences." *Mathematics Teacher* 74 (April 1984): 272–274.

Prielipp, Robert W. "Digital Sums of Perfect Numbers and Triangular Numbers." *Mathematics Teacher* 62 (March 1969): 179–182.

Smith, Joe K. "The *N*th Polygonal Number." *Mathematics Teacher* 65 (March 1972): 221–225.

D. Pi

Apostol, Tom. *The Story of Pi.* (Computer-animated videotape.) Washington, DC: National Council of Teachers of Mathematics, 1989.

Bardis, Panos D. "Evolution of Pi: An Essay in Mathematical Progress from the Great Pyramid to ENIAC." *School Science and Mathematics* 60 (January 1960): 73–78.

Beckman, Petr. *A History of Pi*, 2nd ed. Boulder, CO: The Golem Press, 1971.

Briggs, William L. "Lessons from the Greeks and Computers." *Mathematics Magazine* 55 (January 1982): 19–25.

Davis, James. "An Evening with Pi." *Journal of Recreational Mathematics* 13 (1981): 197–203.

Donahue, Richard. "Estimating Pi by Microcomputer." *Mathematics Teacher* 81 (March 1988): 203–206, 226.

Dudley, Underwood. "π." *Journal of Recreational Mathematics* 9 (1977): 178–180.

_____ . "π: 1832–1879." *Mathematics Magazine* 35 (May 1962):153–154.

Einhorn, Erwin. "A Method for Approximating the Value of Pi with a Computer Application." *Mathematics Teacher* 66 (May 1973): 427–430.

Eves, Howard. "The Latest About Pi." *Mathematics Teacher* 55 (February 1962): 129–30.

Hatcher, Robert S. "Some Little-Known Recipes for Pi." *Mathematics Teacher* 66 (May 1973): 470–474.

Lotspeich, Richard. "Archimedes' Pi—An Introduction to Iteration." *Mathematics Teacher* 81 (March 1988): 208–210.

Maor, Eli. "The History of Pi on the Pocket Calculator." *Journal of College Science Teaching* (November 1976): 97–99.

Moakes, A. J. "The Calculation of Pi." *Mathematical Gazette* 54 (1970): 261–264.

Puritz, C. W. "An Elementary Method of Calculating Pi." *Mathematical Gazette* 58 (1974): 102–108.

Read, Cecil B. "Historical Oddities Relating to the Number Pi." *School Science and Mathematics* 60 (April 1960): 348–350.

_____ . "Shanks, Pi, and Coincidence." *Mathematics Teacher* 60 (December 1967): 761–762.

Shilgalis, Thomas W. "Archimedes and Pi." *Mathematics Teacher* 82 (March 1989): 204-206.

Smithson, Thomas W. "An Eulerian Development for Pi: A Research Project for High School Students." *Mathematics Teacher* 63 (November 1970): 597–608.

Srinevasan, P. K. "Sighting the Value of Pi." *Mathematics Teacher* 74 (May 1981): 380–384.

Wrench, John W., and David Taylor. "The Evolution of Extended Decimal Approximations to Pi." *Mathematics Teacher* 53 (October 1960): 644–650.

Zerger, Monte. "The Magic of Pi." *Journal of Recreational Mathematics* 12 (1979): 21–23.

E. The Golden Ratio

Boles, Martha, and Rochelle Newman. *The Golden Relationship.* Bradford, MA. Pythagorean Press, 1987.

Billstein, Rick, and Johnny Lott. "Golden Rectangles and Ratios." *Student Mathematics Notes* (September 1986).

Brown, Stephen. "From the Golden Rectangle and Fibonacci to Pedagogy and Problem Solving." *Mathematics Teacher* 69 (March 1976): 180–188.

Fischler, Roger. "How to Find the 'Golden Number' Without Really Trying." *Fibonacci Quarterly* 19 (1971): 406–10.

_____ . *A Mathematical History of Division in Extreme and Mean Ratio*. Waterloo, Canada: Wilfrid Laurier University Press, 1987.

Fowler, D. H. "A Generalization of the Golden Section." *Fibonacci Quarterly* 20 (1982): 146–158.

Huntley, H. E. *The Drive Proportion*. New York: Dover Publications, 1970.

Linn, Charles F. *The Golden Mean*. Garden City, NY: Doubleday, 1963.

Markowsky, George. "Misconceptions About the Golden Ratio." *The College Mathematics Journal* 23 (January 1992): 2–19.

Pappas, Theoni. *The Joy of Mathematics*. San Carlos, CA: Wide World Publishing, 1989.

Raab, Joseph. "The Golden Rectangle and Fibonacci Sequence as Related to the Pascal Triangle." *Mathematics Teacher* 55 (November 1962): 538–543.

Rigby, J. F. "Equilateral Triangles and the Golden Ratio." *The Mathematical Gazette* 72 (1988): 27–30.

Runion, Garth E. *The Golden Section and Related Curiosa*. Glenview, IL: Scott, Foresman and Co., 1972.

Seitz, Donald T. "A Geometric Figure Relating the Golden Ratio and Pi." *Mathematics Teacher* 79 (May 1986): 340–41.

Vorob'ev, N. N. *Fibonacci Numbers*. New York: Blaisdell, 1961.

Index

— C —

— Q —

— R —